366
BEDTIME
STORIES

Brown Watson

ENGLAND

Published in Great Britain by
Brown Watson (Leicester) Ltd.,
55a London Road, Leicester.

By arrangement with Pestalozzi-Verlag.

ISBN 0 7097 0634 0

Printed in Czechoslovakia.

50 049

1st January

The Little Sandman (1)

As you know, the little Sandman comes in the evening, and sprinkles sleeping-sand into children's eyes. Then, when the children get tired, the adults say, "The little Sandman was there." But no one has ever seen him. So Lisa and Walter decided to catch the little man. The next evening they went off to bed and closed their eyes tight. But the little Sandman didn't let himself be cheated, and he sprinkled more sand than usual into their eyes. They didn't wake up until the sun was already high in the sky. Just on this day, a little bird wandered into their room. Because they wanted to keep the little bird, they put it in a cage and gave it corn and water. But the bird whistled miserably, "Please let me fly away again!" The children felt sorry for it, so they opened the cage and let it fly away.

The Little Sandman

Before supper the children were playing in the meadow. Along came the little bird again and whistled, "Come with me, I want to reward you because you set me free." Curious, Lisa and Walter followed their friend through the wood until they came to a clearing. There they saw the little Sandman. Many little gnomes were carrying sand to him. Then Walter said, "Maybe we can help them!" Because they were kind children, the gnomes took them with them into the mountain. In a cave there, the sleeping sand glistened like pure gold. Each of the children filled a little sack with it. Then the little Sandman took them with him on his journey. They went through streets, villages, wood, and across seas. They threw sleeping sand into the eyes of Indians, Chinese, and people all over the world. At last, they too fell sleepily into bed.

3rd January

The Dear Little Sunny Ray

You children listen to what I say,
Once there was a sunny ray,
Who shone into the world and far away,
Onto the snow of January.
There little Peter an Igloo had built,
And happily he smiled, and gaily looked out.

4th January

Rapunzel (1)

A man and his wife had waited in vain for a child for many years. But in the end

their wish was fulfilled. During the time before the birth of the child, the wife often used to look down from her window into a wonderful garden below. This garden belonged to a terrible witch. One day the wife discovered a bed of wonderful radishes, and she began to have a real craving for them. She said to her husband: "If I can't have some of those radishes, then I will surely die." So her husband went down into the garden one night, and filled a basket full of radishes. Suddenly the furious witch stood before him. "A curse on you!" she cried.

Terrified the man said, "I had to do it! My wife is expecting a child, and she would have died if she couldn't have any!"
The witch replied, "Take as many as you want, but in return, I want the child when it is born." In his fear, the man promised. When the child was born, the witch appeared. She gave it the name of Rapunzel, and took it away with her.

Rapunzel (2)

Rapunzel became the most beautiful child under the sun. The witch shut her in a tower. When she wanted to go into the tower, she shouted, "Rapunzel, Rapunzel, let down your hair." Rapunzel had long, magnificent hair. Whenever she heard the witch's voice, she threw out her hair which reached down twenty feet. Then the witch climbed up. To pass the time, Rapunzel sang. One day, a Prince heard the beautiful singing. He fell in love with the beautiful girl who stood at the tower window, but he didn't know how to reach her. Then one day he saw how the witch climbed up to Rapunzel. When she had gone, he cried, "Rapunzel, Rapunzel, let down your hair." This the girl did and from then on the Prince came to her every day and they were very happy together.

Rapunzel (3)

One day Rapunzel said to the witch, "You cannot climb up as easily as the Prince." The witch knew then that Rapunzel had deceived her, so she cut off her hair. She took the girl to a lonely place. When the Prince next went to the tower and called out to Rapunzel, the witch let down the girl's hair, which she had fastened to a hook. When he reached the room, he found only the witch, She cried, "Rapunzel is lost to you forever, you will never see her again." So the Prince, overcome with grief, leapt from the tower. He survived the fall, but the thorns into which he fell blinded him. He stumbled around the wood, eating nothing except weeds and berries, and mourning his lost love. After a few years he came to the place where Rapunzel was living in misery. Here he heard a voice that was well known to him, and he crawled in the direction of the voice. When Rapunzel saw him, she flung her arms around his neck and cried. One of her tears moistened his blind eyes, and suddenly he could see again. Together they found their way back to the Prince's Kingdom, where they lived happily ever after.

The Nutcracker

Jeremy's grandmother had a nutcracker, with a flower-decorated hat on its head. Every time Jeremy visited his gran, he asked her if he could play with her nut-cracker, and of course she let him. Susan, the little girl from next door, also played with the nutcracker. One day, before Jeremy had played with the nutcracker for very long, he put it back on its shelf, and suddenly went very quiet.

One day, Jeremy's grandmother came to visit, but Jeremy was not as happy as usual. "What's the matter with the child?" asked grandmother.

"Jeremy's not very happy," his mother explained. "He broke the flowers on the nutcracker's hat."

"But they were already broken," said grandmother, "Susan did it the last time she played with him."

Jeremy threw his arms around his gran's neck: "And I was so worried, I couldn't sleep at night."

The Little Cloth Horse

Once upon a time, in a big town, there was a toy shop. Day after day the children

spent hours looking at the wonderful toys in the window. Right in the front stood a small, blue, cloth horse. This little horse kept wishing that someone would buy him. But no one noticed him. Very popular, however, was the doll called Claudia. She had long black plaits, real eyelashes, and a charming little green dress with white spots. Not only the children liked Claudia, but also the other toys in the window, especially a young boy-doll who sat next to her. The puppet, who sat in his puppet theatre, would also have liked to be near Claudia. Sometimes she gave him a friendly nod, but then she would start talking with her neighbour again.

The Little Cloth Horse (2)

"What can I do?" grumbled the puppet, "so that Claudia will notice me?" And so, one midnight, he climbed down from his chair, and went straight to the little blue horse. "Please, little horse, help me. I want to fetch some roses for Claudia from the park, and I can't do it on my own." The little horse was happy that he had been noticed, and he let the puppet sit on his back, while he crept out of the shop through an open door. Then they saw Morris the cat, who came after them. The cat only asked them where they were going, and when he found out he offered to get the roses. It was easy for him to climb up the rose bush, and he picked the most beautiful roses. Claudia was amazed when the puppet gave her real roses, and when she heard the little horse's part in it, she patted him fondly. When the little horse awoke, he still felt someone stroking him. It wasn't the doll, but a little boy, a little boy who was happily carrying his new toy home.

Little Peter (1)

There was once a little boy called Peter, who slept in a wheelbed. When he wasn't tired, his mother would wheel him around the room, and he loved that.

Now one night, Peter just couldn't sleep, and so his mother rocked the bed with her arm from her own bed. But when her arm got tired and she fell asleep, little Peter called, "More, more!" but she did not hear. Before long old Mr. Moon looked in through the window. What he saw there was so funny, he had to wipe his eyes to believe it. There lay little Peter wide awake, with his leg in the air as a mast, and his pyjama top stretched over it to make a sail. Then gradually he began to roll, over the floor, up the wall, over the ceiling and down the other wall again. It was very lucky for little Peter that it was night and that the Earth was standing on its head, otherwise he could have easily broken his neck. When he had done this three times, the moon said to him: "Little

crowed. "What are you doing?" called little Peter. "I'm crowing for the first time," called down the cock. "Where are the people?" called little Peter. "They're sleeping. They won't wake up until I crow for the third time." "I can't wait that long," called little Peter. "I want to go into the wood, I want all the animals to see me." So they rode out of the town, over fields and into the wood. Here it was still and lonely, and no animals were to be seen, except for a cat up in a tree. "Where are all the other animals?" called Peter. "They're asleep," called the cat. "Can't you hear them snoring?"

"Little boy, haven't you had enough yet?" called the moon.

"No, more, more. Shine old moon, shine!" called Peter.

So they rode out of the wood, over the heather and right to the end of the world, and into the sky.

boy, haven't you had enough yet?"

"More, more!" was the reply. "Open the door, I want to go into the street. I want everyone to see me."

"I can't open the door," said the moon. But he let a bright ray shine through the keyhole, and on this ray little Peter rode away.

11th January

Little Peter (2)

Out in the street it was very still. The big houses just stood there in the bright moonlight. No one was to be seen. The wheel-bed rattled loudly over the cobblestones. When they rode past the church, the big golden cock on the tower

It was good fun up there! All the stars were awake and shining. The cat rode into the crowd of stars, so that they fell from the sky in fear. Suddenly, Peter rode right over the nose of the good moon, so that he became completely dark. Out went his lantern and all the stars closed their eyes. Because it was so dark in the sky, little Peter became very frightened. Then finally, deep down in the sky, a round red face stared up at him. It was the sun. "Little boy!" she called. "What are you doing here in my sky?" She took little Peter and flung him into the sea. And what do you think happened? If you and I hadn't come in our little boat, he would have drowned!

Winter Lullaby

Go to sleep, my little child,
Don't listen to the wind outside.
He's singing the whole world off to sleep,
While you from warm soft covers peep.
And if he blows at you, don't cry,
Just listen to my lullaby.

Go to sleep, my little child,
Don't listen to the wind outside.
Close to the window you'll hear him creep,
He looks for children who will not sleep,
And if he finds one, he takes a ladle,
And sprinkles cold snow over their cradle.

Go to sleep, my little child,
Don't listen to the wind outside.
He rustles through the dark trees green,
And whispers quietly a wonderful dream.
Gaily he hums and gaily he sings,
And murmurs to children what Santa will bring.

Go to sleep, my little child,
Don't listen to the wind outside.
Then suddenly the sun cries,
"Good day!"
And Spring chases the noisy wind away.
The children's cheeks turn rosy red,
And all the Earth wakes from its bed.

Go to sleep, my little child,
Don't listen to the wind outside.

Casper Caffrey (1)

stands a chest. Casper quickly goes home to fetch his friend Steve, and he takes him back to where he found the chest. "Isn't it beautiful!" says Casper.

This crown is meant for a fairy King, and this dwarf is working on it in his cave. Suddenly along comes a wicked wizard, who wants the dwarf's treasure. He creeps up to the unsuspecting dwarf, and murmering "Hocuspocus", he forces the magic cap onto his head from behind, and the dwarf becomes a cricket. The wizard takes the animal and shuts it up in the wood, and after that he hurries back to get the dwarf's treasure. While this was happening, Casper Caffrey was looking for some mushrooms in the wood. Suddenly he bumps into something. In the middle of the path

Steve is fascinated, and both of them set to work. They push it over to the car, and with great trouble they lift it in. When they get back to the house, Gretel is already waiting for them. It was certainly not easy to bring the chest into the house. It falls and burst open. Meanwhile, Wobble Ears the little rabbit, has got free, and Gretel is trying to catch it. Casper and Steve also try to catch the rabbit. But the rabbit hops into the chest. Steve takes it out, but as soon as he has it, another rabbit appears, and this goes on until they all have their arms full of rabbits!

Casper Caffrey (2)

While these three are completely occupied with the rabbits, the Wizard discovers that his magic chest has disappeared, but because he is a wizard he knows exactly where it is. He makes a horse out of a dry branch, and quickly rides to Casper's house. He gets down in front of the door, casts another spell, and the horse disappears. Then the Wizard goes into Casper's house, and at first can't see anything for rabbits. When Casper sees him, he can't imagine who this strange man is. The Wizard closes the chest, says "Hocus pocus", and all the rabbits disappear again. But look! Both Casper and Steve now have ears like rabbits. They look at each other terrified, while the Wizard climbs back into his chest, and rolls in it out of the open door. When Gretel comes back, she takes a pair of scissors and wants to cut their ears off. But neither of them want that for it is bound to hurt, so they run out of the house, into the car, and drive out into the wood. They stop right at the spot where

the poor cricket is living. The cricket calls: "Oh, please, set me free!" Casper sets the little creature free straight away, and the cricket was full of joy. Then the Wizard hears them. Qucily the cricket flies to a tree, and manages to pull the magic cap from his bald head. Without this hat the Wizard has no power. Quickly the cricket puts the cap onto Steve's and Casper's head, so that the huge ears

shrink to their normal size. "Now it's my turn!" cries the cricket, and when the cap is put over him, it spins like a top, and then it disappears. In its place now stands the fairy goldsmith. Meanwhile the Wizard is searching in despair for his cap, and as he approaches the cage, Casper pushes him in. And there he sits to this very day.

15th January

Hans isn't Hungry

"Hans, come in, it's dinner-time," calls mother. But Hans isn't hungry. He never feels very hungry. At dinner, Han's father asks, "How would you like to spend a few days with your friend Robert?" Hans was very pleased, for it was great fun at Robert's house, there were so many children there. The next day they go over to Robert's, who is playing with his brothers and sisters in the garden. Hans can't wait to play too. He hardly notices when his mother goes, he is having such fun. "Everyone come in, it's dinner time!" calls Robert's mother. Robert and his brothers and sisters drop everything and stream into the house. Hans is taken aback at first, and then runs in behind them. He eats just as well as the other children. When mummy comes back, Hans has round red cheeks. "I need a few brothers and sisters," says Hans, "because then food tastes much much better!"

16th January

Little Joe Looks for Friends (1)

In the distant morning land lives little Joe. He lives completely alone in a big house with many rooms and big gardens. You'd think he would be very happy there, but no, little Joe is sad. "Ah! If only I had a few playmates, then it wouldn't be so lonely here," he sighs. "Hey! I have it. I'll fly into the world and look for friends!" He fetches his magic carpet and flies away. Down on the streets, the people point excitedly into the sky. A brightly-coloured bird flies ahead. "Please little Joe," he twitters, "please take me with you on your carpet, my little wings are so tired I can't fly any longer."

"Of course," says little Joe. "Do you want to be my playmate?"

"Oh yes," twitters the little bird. "My name is Tom". After a while, little Joe looks down, and he catches sight of a beautiful island below him. "That's where we want to go!" he calls, "maybe we'll find another playmate there!" Little Joe orders his carpet to put him down on the island, and the carpet sweeps slowly down.

17th January

Little Joe Looks for Friends (2)

On the island is a big palm tree, and in the palm lives a little monkey called Jojo, who plucks coconuts. He sees Joe and the little bird Tom coming on the carpet, and plop! – he throws a coconut at them. "Hey! Who's throwing coconuts at me?" says Joe.

"What are you doing under my palm tree then?" asks Jojo.

"I'm looking for a playmate," says Joe. "Woudln't you like to fly with me to my big house?" "I'd love to," says Jojo, "as long as I can take a coconut with me on the journey". He climbed down the big palm tree, sat down next to Joe and the bird, and they flew away. The carpet swept over seas, mountains and towns. Finally beneath them lay the desert. Suddenly Joe heard a low soft wimpering below him. They quickly landed. It was a lion who was crying and licking his paw. "I stood on a thorn and can't pull it out. It's stuck so deep. Can't you help me?" he wailed. "I know!" said little Tom, "I'll get it out with my beak!" And before Baba, the little lion, knew what was happening, the thorn was gone.

"Don't you want to come with us to be our playmate?" asks Joe. The lion happily agrees, so they fly back on the carpet to Morning Land.

You can imagine what a happy life they had. The four friends are always up to tricks in the big house and gardens, but that's another story.

11

The hedgehog and the hare (1)

It was a Sunday in Autumn. The hedgehog stood before his door and hummed a tune. It occurred to him that

while his wife was washing and dressing the children, he could go for a walk somewhere in the fields and see how the turnips passed the time. On his way he met the hare. The hedgehog wished him good morning. But the hare, who was a very proud gentleman, did not return the greeting, but said to him, "How is it you're walking about in the fields so early: I think you could use your legs for better things." This answer annoyed the hedgehog, for he couldn't get about as

well as he would have liked, because his legs were so crooked. "So you imagine your legs are better?" he said to the hare. "Yes I think so," the other replied. "If we had a race, I would win." "Oh no you wouldn't!" replied the hedgehog angrily. "What would you bet?" "A golden coin and a bottle of wine," said the hare. "Done!" said the hedgehog and they arranged to meet up in half an hour. As the hedgehog was walking home, he said to himself: "He thinks he's such a fine gentleman, but I'll teach him a lesson!"

The hedgehog and the hare (2)

When the hedgehog got home, he said to his wife, "Get dressed quickly and come with me into the fields. I've bet the hare that I can run quicker than he can!" "Have you lost your reason!" exclaimed his wife. "Be quiet, woman!" replied the hedgehog. "Put a pair of my trousers on and come with me!" What could she do? She had to go whether she wanted to or not. On the way the hedgehog said to his wife. "Look over there on that field, that's where we're going to race. The hare will run in that furrow and I'll run in the other. All you have to do is stand down here in the furrow. When the hare comes, call

ut to him, 'I'm here already!'" So the
ife stood in her furrow, and the
edgehog walked up to the top of the
eld. The hare was already there. On the
ount of three the race began, and the
are ran like the wind down the field. But
he hedgehog only took three steps, and

en sat down quietly in the furrow.
When the hare reached the other end of
e field, the wife called out, "I'm already
ere!" The hare was taken aback. He
nought it was the hedgehog himself
ho called to him, for the wife looked
xactly like her husband. "That's not
ght!" he said. "Let's race again," and he
ore off down the field. He did this thirty-
even times, and each time the
edgehog or his wife called out, "I'm
lready there". Finally the hare collapsed
n the ground, but the hedgehog took his
innings, and walked happily home with
is wife.

Christine King's Distant Journey

Christine King stands in front of her
mother's wardrobe, and pulls out all
kinds of marvellous clothes. An
enormous hat, with flowers on it, a
fragrant slip with many layers of lace, a
cape and mummy's dancing shoes.
Quickly Christine slips into the lace slip
and looks proudly at herself in the mirror.
She puts the hat on her head and the cape
around her shoulders. Where is
mummy's lipstick? An elegant lady is
always well made-up. In the end she
finds mummy's make-up bag. Christine

uses everything she can find. Content,
she looks at herself in the mirror. Now
Christine is going on a journey, for she
wants to be seen around the town.
Maybe she'll even go to Africa, or to the
sea. Hopefully mummy won't come until
Christine has gone. But mummy comes
just as she is going out the door, and she
says: "Christine, that skirt is much too
long for you". The journey has been
postponed.

21st January

What Happened to Stubborn Peter

Peter cried out angrily, "I don't want to!"
"Then I don't want to either," says his puppet, and runs out of the door.
"I'm not going to either!" says his ball, and rolls out after the puppet, closely followed by the bear. But that's not all! The plates hop away from the table, quickly followed by the spoons and the forks. Peter tries to stop the table-cloth, but this is as stubborn as he, and cries, "If you don't want to, you naughty boy, then neither do I!" Peter is very upset, and sits down very quietly, then suddenly he jumps up and shouts at the top of his voice, "I will, I will, I will!"

22nd January

Little Brother and Sister (1)

The brother took his sister by the hand and said, "Ever since mother died times

have been bad. Our stepmother beats u every day, and only gives us breadcrust to eat. Come on, let's go out into th world." All day they wandered ove meadows and fields, and in the evenin came to a big forest. They were so tire with misery and hunger, that they sa down in a hollow tree and went to sleep

The next day when they woke up, th brother said: "Little sister, I'm thirsty So, hand in hand, they went off to look fc water. The wicked stepmother, howeve was a witch, and had cursed every sprin in the forest. When they came to stream, a voice called out, "Whoeve drinks me will become a deer!" But th little brother was so thirsty, that he ber

14

own and drank. As soon as the water touched his lips, he turned into a deer. The little sister cried bitterly and said: "Don't be sad, I'll never leave you!" Then she took off her golden garter, and laid it round the deer's neck. They wandered through the forest until they came to an empty house. Here they stayed, and the little sister made it as homely as she could.

23rd January

Little Brother and Sister (2)

It came to pass that the King of the land held a big hunt in the forest. The deer, of course, wanted to be there, and at last the little sister gave in to his pleas. "When you come back," she said. "Knock three times and say 'Little sister, let me in!'" And so the deer sprang happily into the forest. The hunters saw the beautiful beast, but they couldn't catch it. When it was dark, the deer went back to the house, knocked three times and said, "Little sister, let me in!" One of the hunters had seen everything, and he told the King. The next day in the forest, the King followed the deer, and when he knocked on the door and was let in, the King went in behind him. The girl he saw there was so beautiful that he fell in love with her and asked her to be his wife. The little sister gladly accepted, but only on condition that the deer could go with them. The King agreed, and he took the girl to his castle, where the marriage was celebrated with great pomp. Now when the wicked stepmother heard how happy the brother and sister were, jealousy and evil rose in her heart. She tried to think of a way she could spoil it all for them.

24th January

Little Brother and Sister (3)

The stepmother thought that her own daughter should have been Queen. Now that the little sister had just had a beautiful little baby, the King was out hunting again. The old witch took on the form of the Lady-in-waiting and said to the ill Queen, ''Come, I've prepared a bath for you that will bring you strength.''

The old witch and her daughter put the Queen into her bath. But they had made it so hot that the Queen fainted in the steam. The ugly daughter of the stepmother got into bed instead of the Queen, for she had been given the Queen's form. At night the real Queen came into the child's bedroom, and drew the child to her heart, and then disappeared again. The nurse had seen everything, and she told the King. The next night the King stayed up all night

with his child and, sure enough, there appeared the real Queen. Happily she took the King in her arms, and the witch and her daughter were banished from the kingdom, then the deer turned back into the little brother. They all lived happily ever after.

25th January

A Hard Winter

All the world is covered in snow,
It's so very cold but there's nowhere t
go,
No birds sing and no flowers grow,
Hunger hurts, and the wind does blow.

The beggars limp round dirty bins,
The dogs lick meat from empty tins,
Brothers in hunger with no warmth c
cheer,
Their backs to the wind while winter'
here.

But don't despair for Spring is there,
Waiting to bring back the weather fair,
Then berries will bloom for mile afte
mile,
The plants will grow and people wi
smile.

26th January

Black Mary

You all know the story about Gold Ma
and Black Mary? Of course you want t

know what happened to Black Mary; well, I can tell you. Nobody wanted anything to do with her, for whoever touched her immediately became black. So her mother prepared a warm bath for her and hoped that Black Mary would become white again. But no! The longer she stayed in the water, the blacker it became, and Black Mary stayed just as black as before. One day a scholar came into Black Mary's house. He wanted to learn the truth of the story and to note down all the details. As he was just about to write, he noticed he had forgotten his pen. So he dipped a pointed piece of wood into the bath water, and found he could write perfectly well with it. So he had a big barrel brought which he filled with the water, and had it taken home. This he did every Sunday from then on, for Black Mary had a bath every Sunday. For every barrel Black Mary got a golden coin, and in this way she earned her living. The scholar made up a name for this black liquid — ink!

27th January

At the Woodcutter's House (1)

In the wood stands a woodcutter's house, where the woodcutter Claude and his wife Elizabeth live with his dog, who's very nice and not at all stupid except that he's got a crooked tail and crooked legs!

At the Woodcutter's House (2)

The mouse comes out. After the mouse springs the cat, after the cat springs the dog, and pecking at the dog's tail comes the raven! The Woodcutter takes a stick and tries to beat off the raven. "Oh no!"

Also in the house lives a cat called Ludo, a raven, and a cock with his seventy hens, the names of whom I won't begin to mention! On the roof lives a stork who comes from Africa, and his wife Margaret. In the cellar lives a little grey mouse, who Ludo knows only too well!

But the mouse is crafty and won't let himself be caught so easily, and he's never been caught in the mousetrap either. But one day when the mouse comes out of his hole, peace rules no more! Why? What happens? Well, I'll tell you tomorrow.

cries his wife, and chases them all out into the hen-yard. The hens run up and down and all around, while the cock perches himself on the manure heap, because he feels safe there. The stork in his nest just looks down peacefully on the havoc below. The mouse turns round and runs back into the house. When the wife sees it, she jumps on a chair and screams. So you see a little mouse can bring the most fear of all. The mouse goes back into its hole, and peace reigns once more. The woodcutter sits down while his wife goes straight to bed after her shock!

29th January

Woody's Secret

You would think a little dog would have no secrets. Well, Woody has! Woody is the forester's best friend, but one day he escaped into the wood, playing with his ball. Suddenly it disappeared down a hole which led down into the ground. He put in his snout and sniffed. What a funny smell! Suddenly a black nose appeared, followed by a small rust-red animal. All five of them began to play with the ball in a little clearing, and they completely forgot the time. When Woody finally ran back to the forester's house, it was already dark. "Woody!" called the forester. "Where have you been all this time?" But Woody didn't betray anything, he just wagged his tail and barked. But the forester didn't understand, and he never found the foxes hiding-place – that is Woody's secret!

30th January

Tommy Goes Shopping

''Are we having cakes?'' asks Tommy. ''Yes,'' answers his mother, ''But I still need all the ingredients. Could you quickly run to get them? I need half a pound of butter, a pound of sugar, a pound of flour, three eggs and baking powder.''

Tommy sets off and keeps repeating the ingredients to himself as he goes along. When he has bought everything, he hurries back home and lays everything on the table, the sugar, the butter, the flour and the eggs, and he wants to start making the cake. Tommy's mother notices he has forgotten something, but what? Did you notice he had forgotten the baking powder? Without that the cake wouldn't be nice at all.

his mother couldn't see him, and carried on playing with his ball. Then his ball rolled down a hill, and Peter followed it. Soon he didn't recognise the houses anymore, but he discovered a playground, and he went in and played with the other children. Soon, however, they had to go home too, and he was suddenly alone. Full of fear he ran onto the street and sobbed. Then a good friend of his parents came by.

''Are you lost?'' he said. ''Then come with me.'' And he took the rascal back home, where mummy and daddy were already very worried. They were as relieved as Peter that he was back home.

31st January

Peter the Runaway

Near me lives a little boy called Peter. ''Peter!'' calls his mother in the evenings, ''Come in, it's supper time!'' But one summer evening, Peter didn't want to go in, so he ran off down the street so that

1st February

The Dear Little Sunny Ray

On a snowy day in February,
Through the clouds came our sunny ray.
There by the woodcutter's houses,
covered in snow,
He saw little Tina feeding a doe,
Brightly he shone, and sunnily he smiled,
And lit up the house of the good-hearted child.

2nd February

The Sleepy Sandman

"Atichoo!" sneezed the Sandman. "I must check how much sand I have left in my bag," he said. But no sooner had he opened the bag when he had to sneeze again, so that so much sand flew into his eyes that he yawned loudly and fell asleep. A dwarf came and found him. He tried in vain to wake the Sandman. "What shall I do?" whispered the dwarf. But then he had an idea and he quickly called all the birds together, who were already sitting in their nests.

"Listen, little birds," said the dwarf. "Can you sprinkle sand in the children's eyes tonight."

"Of course," they twittered, and they each took as much sand as they could in their beaks and sprinkled it in the children's eyes who were all crying, awake in their beds. And so it happened that, on this day, the birds put the children to sleep.

3rd February

Mark's Magic Drawing Book (1)

Diane could draw wonderfully, and she always had new ideas. There, in her drawing book, sat her teddy bear, near Lisa the doll and the baby holding its bottle in the cradle. Or she had drawn herself on her scooter with her hair flying out behind her with her little brother Mark running behind her. Especially nice was her picture of the Princess Marzipan meeting the Prince Coconut. Mark,

21

however, could not draw very well and he was used to copying from his sisters pictures. But one day Diane slammed her book shut and said, "I'm not going to let you look any more." Now Mark chewed on his pencil and eventually began to cry. Meanwhile Diane had drawn a new picture of some animals she had seen in the zoo. The fat elephant, the long giraffe and a few funny monkeys.

4th February

Mark's Magic Drawing Book (2)

So when it was night time and both children were tucked up in bed, something very strange happened. Princess Marzipan called all the figures out of the pictures together. "I feel sorry for Mark. I say we should all walk into his drawing book so that he will always have figures to copy. Diane can draw new

pictures. "Everyone agreed. And s began the procession into the othe drawing book, and what fun it was Prince Coconut waltzed along. The kin fetched all the bananas from his castl and fed the monkeys, and the bab wanted the Queen to change his napp Soon it became bright outside and th Princess told everyone to hurry and fin themselves in the book. When Dian came down to breakfast she got a shoc when she opened her drawing book Every page was empty except for on page on which lay Princess Marzipan' crown which she had lost. But Mar picked up his book and wanted to burs out laughing. Instead of the dolls sa three monkeys around the table, and th fourth was peeping out of the dolls cradle, where the puppet had also mad himself comfortable. On the next pag was the giraffe looking down from th castle. The thin queen was sitting behin a cage in the zoo, the teddy bear ha

taken the baby's bottle and then the elephant took it and was drinking out of it. The elephant swung himself onto Diane's scooter and zoomed through the park. Panting, the little king ran behind him and tried to catch him up, "Wait for me, he cried, "I want a ride too," But the elephant couldn't stop and so the fat little king kept running behind him.

At the top of the tree sat the squawking parrot, who flapped his wings wildly around him. So now Mark had enough ideas of things to copy, and he eagerly set to work and took great trouble to put everything in its proper place in a new book. And Diane? Well, she soon thought of new pictures to draw and her empty drawing book is already full again.

The Maharaji from Kajahari (1)

The Maharaji from Kajahari lived in India in a beauitful palace. In the palace yard lived a tame elephant who was very content because he got good and rich food.　　　　Only now and again, when the Maharaji wanted to go on a trip, did he have anything to do. Then he was richly decorated so that the townspeople noticed straight away that the noble Maharaji was coming. The rest of the court had to come too of course! The head chef, the scribe, the waterpipe holder, the palace guard, the fly catcher, and the head wife. What a crown on the elephant's back. The Maharaji and the head wife had the best seats, of course. They sat under a canopy and had fresh air fanned on them. And so the Maharaji and the whole court trundled contentedly through the land.

missed so much the young fres[h]
vegetables, the plentiful loads of hay, an[d]
the tender palm leaves. How his mou[th]
watered when he thought about all thes[e]
lovely things. So the elephant trampe[d]
sadly on and lost more and more weig[ht]
until he became a very thin elephant. B[ut]
the Maharaji missed his form[er]
companion too and he sent out a sear[ch]
party to look for him. They brought t[he]

The Maharaji from Kajahari (2)

The elephant carried the company over paths, streets and bridges. On the edge of one street sat a little boy with a toy mouse in his hand. He turned a key and the mouse ran towards the elephant. *"Waagh!"* with a powerful leap the elephant shot off in terror. And all his passengers nearly fell off. Just look what happened. After the elephant had taken another jump, the first one lost his balance and tumbled down. From the front fell the cook, followed by the scribe and the waterpipe holder. From behind fell the palace guard, and finally the Maharaji and his favourite wife. But the elephant ran and ran until he was out of sight. From now on the Maharaji travelled in a carriage. The poor elephant meanwhile had got lost. He ran through the whole land looking for his master, but he couldn'f find him anywhere. He

thin elephant back to his stall and fed him richly. How happy the elephant was! And look – it didn't take long to make him fat again.

7th February

The Frog King (1)

Long ago, when wishes came true, there lived a King whose daughters were very beautiful. But the most beautiful was the youngest. Near the castle was a big dark forest, and in the forest near an old oak tree was a pond. The Princess often used to sit by the edge of this pond, and if she got bored she would play with a golden ball. That was her favourite toy. But one day she dropped the ball and it rolled into the water. The Princess tried to find it, but the water was so deep she couldn't see it, and she began to cry and couldn't stop. Suddenly a voice called "What's wrong, little Princess? You are crying enough to melt a stone." And when she looked around she saw the fat ugly head of a frog poking out of the water. "I'm crying over my golden ball that fell into the pond.

"Don't cry," said the frog. "I'll help you. But what will you give me if I bring it back to you?"

"Anything you want."

"I want you to love me, to let me eat from your plate, sit next to you at table, drink from your cup, and sleep in your bed. If you promise me that I'll help you." The Princess promised and soon she had the golden ball in her hand again and was running away with it.

The Frog King (2)

After the Princess had got her ball back she forgot her promises. But the next day when she was sitting at the table with her family – *plitsch, platsch* – something was coming up the marble stairs. Then it knocked at the door and called "Open up, Princess." But as soon as she saw the frog, she slammed the door shut again. "Why are you so frightened?" asked the King. So she told him what had happened. Then the King looked at her with a grave face. "You must keep your promises. Now go and open the door to him." When she opened the door the frog hopped in and demanded to be put on the table. As soon as he was on the table he began to eat from the Princess's plate, and when he had finished he said, "Now I am full up and tired. Take me to your room." The Princess began to cry, but the King said angrily "Whoever helps you in a time of need you have to take care of." So she led the frog to her room with a heavy heart. And as she was going to bed the frog croaked. "I want to sleep just as well as you.." Then she became angry, so she picked him up and threw him with all her might against the wall. But as he fell to the floor, there stood a prince in his place.

The Frog King (3)

An ugly frog had turned into a handsom prince! The princess asked him i astonishment where he had come from "I was the frog you threw against th wall," said the prince, smiling. "An angr witch put a curse on me and I could neve had been freed unless someone let m eat from their plate, drink from their cu and sleep in their bed. If your fathe hadn't been a good and wise king an made you keep your promise, 1 woul have never have been set free." Th princess looked at the prince with love Then she took his hand and led him t her father. A splendid wedding took plac that lasted for four weeks and all th people in the land were invited. On morning along came a splendid carriag with six white horses to take the youn couple to the prince's kingdom. Ther they lived happily ever after.

reamy Tony (1)

led him into his orchard where many oranges grew. Little girls filled huge baskets with the oranges they had just plucked. Tony could hardly believe that he was really in Italy. He even helped pick the oranges.

Dreamy Tony (2)

he teacher, Mr Plum, talked about Italy Geography lessons and had shown any pictures to the class. Tony was so scinated by all this that he dreamt of aly during the whole lesson. On his way ome he went through the market square here there were many foreign cars. uddenly along came a small curly-aired girl who pushed a beautiful range into his hand. It was just the kind f orange that grows in Italy. Overjoyed, ony ran up the mountain, to his house, here the goats were grazing. There he y down on the grass and along came lob the hamster who looked in mazement at the golden orange. Tony's yes too were bigger and bigger as the range began to grow. Tony climbed nto it and floated off. Along with him ent the Swallow family. The orange oated off to Italy. Beneath him Tony saw nountain villages, and the orange sank own over one of these villages. The range landed right in front of a small ellow house and began to shrink until ony could quite easily put it in his ocket. Then a friendly man came out of e house and invited Tony to stay with im. Tony gladly accepted, and the man

Everyone helped with the orange harvest. The girls packed every orange carefully so that none were squashed. Meanwhile it had grown dark, and now that the work was over everyone wanted to relax and enjoy themselves. The whole villages met down at the harbour, and a great party began. In the sky sparkled Catherine wheels and rockets. Tony's friends sang with a mandolin and Tony danced with the girls. Brightly coloured lanterns glistened softly in the warm wind. Next morning the orange farmer took Tony to a beautiful town. There instead of streets were canals which flowed by white palaces and upon which gondolas swayed. Then they came to a huge square where there were many people feeding the pigeons. Then Tony's orange began to grow again. He had to climb on very quickly and just had time to

say goodbye to his astonished friends as he flew home. The orange shrank again .. . and Tony woke up. The goats looked at him questioningly and Tony wondered what they know about his journey on the orange. But it had been wonderful!

12th February

The Pigeon and the Cat

The pigeon sat upon a roof,
A cat, pretending to be aloof,
Washed his paws and slyly watched him

The cat crept up with his claws spread out,
But the bird just flew to another house!

13th February

Blackie the Little Donkey

A little black donkey was born in a zoo. A the other animals were astonishe because donkeys are usually grey. Th zoo keeper was also very pleased an called the donkey Blackie. Blackie' mother pulled a gaily coloured cart an brought children in it to visit the zoo When I grow up, I'd like to do that too thought Blackie. The next day Blacki was woken up by the parrots. "Wake up The circus master is here to buy som animals." And before Blackie knew wha

was happening he was led away by the man. When he went into the circus wagon he was really sad. But when little Stevie, the circus master's son, lovingly put his arms around him he felt better. Soon the circus took down its huge tents and the brightly painted wagons rolled towards another town.

Blackie was taught many tricks, and was put into the show. Next spring Blackie was allowed back to the zoo for he had grown too big. Blackie was happy. Now he takes children for walks in that gaily coloured wagon.

14th February

The Golden Goose (1)

There was once a man who had three sons. The youngest was called Dumpling and everyone mocked him. Now one day the eldest son went into the forest to chop wood. To help him on his way his mother gave him three buns and a bottle of wine for his lunch. In the forest he met a little grey man who asked him for something to eat, but the lad did not want

to share his food. Soon afterwards his axe slipped and cut his arm deeply. Afterwards along went the second son into the forest with the same food, and the same little man came along and asked him for something to eat. But the second son said "If I give you something to eat that means less for me. Be off with you."

After he had cut up a few logs, he hacked himself in the leg and had to be carried home. And so Dumpling said, "Father, let me go out and chop wood." After some persuasion his father agreed, and his mother packed him off with dry biscuits and sour beer. When the little grey man asked for food and drink Dumpling gladly shared it. The dried biscuits became sweet buns and the sour beer red wine. "Because you have a good heart I will bring you good luck," said the little man. "Cut down that tree over there and see what you find." Then the little man said goodbye. Dumpling cut down the tree and found a golden goose. He put it under his arm and went to an inn to stay the night. But the Innkeeper had three daughters who took a liking to the goose. When the eldest daughter tried to take one of its feathers she got stuck to it. The second daughter tried to set her sister free but when she touched her she was also stuck. The same thing happened to the third daughter. The next morning Dumpling marched away with his goose and took no notice of the long tail he was pulling behind him.

15th February

The Golden Goose (2)

On the field he met the priest. Shocked to see the girls running after a young man, the priest took hold of one of them and tried to pull her back. But as soon as he touched her the priest also got stuck and had to run on behind the girls. Then the priest's belper caught sight of the strange band and he called "Priest, where are you going in such a hurry?" You've got to perform a baptism.'' He ran up to the priest and grabbed him by the shoulder. But as soon as he had touched him he, of course, got stuck. As the five were marching along behind each other, two farmers came from the field in amazement. The two farmers tried to free the priests, but as soon as they touched them they got stuck and couldn't get free again. That made seven people who were running after Dumpling and the goose. Soon afterwards they came to a town where there was a king who had a daughter. In her whole life this princess had never laughed. The king had promised that the man who made her laugh could have her hand in marriage. When Dumpling heard this he went with his procession into the castle and presented himself to the princess. When she caught sight of the strange company she began to laugh and laugh. Now Dumpling went to the king and demanded the Princess for his bride. But the king didn't think Dumpling was good enough for his daughter and he set several tasks for Dumpling to do before he could have her.

The Golden Goose (3)

First of all the king demanded that Dumpling bring him a man who could drink a whole wine cellar dry. Dumpling thought of the little grey man and he went into the forest to look for him. When he got to the place where he had cut down the tree, he found there a man with a very sad face. "I am so thirsty," complained the man "and no one can satisfy my thirst." Dumpling took him to

the king's cellar and by evening all the barrels were empty. But still the king didn't want to give up his daughter. "Bring me a man who can eat a mountain of bread," demanded the King. Dumpling went back to the forest and there he found a man sitting on a tree stump who grumbled "I am so hungry and no one can satisfy me." When Dumpling heard that, he took the man to the king's palace.

The king had had an enormous mountain of bread baked. But the man quickly set about it and after a day and night the whole mountain had disappeared. The king would not part with his daughter yet and he ordered Dumpling to build a ship that travelled over both land and sea. In the forest this time Dumpling met the little grey man himself and because Dumpling had such a good heart the little grey man gave him such a ship. When the king saw it he knew he could not keep his daughter from Dumpling any longer. Dumpling married the princess and after the king's death Dumpling inherited the kingdom and reigned there wisely and justly.

17th February

The Polar Bear and the Brown Bear

Once upon a time in a zoo lived a polar bear and a brown bear next door to each other. "Where I come from," said the polar bear, "everything is as white as me. Only the sky is blue when it is not snowing."

"How wonderful," exclaimed the little brown bear. "Everything white and clean. That sounds like the place for me, then I would be able to stop having to wash everything that I eat. What do they eat in your country?"

"Fish," said the polar bear licking his lips, "fish is the best!" "Of course," agreed the brown bear "but fruit maize and other plants are good too. They are the best," said the brown bear with longing eyes.

"But fish is the best," repeated the polar bear.

The two bears began to quarrel about which food really tasted the best. They got so angry that in the end they wouldn't speak to each other anymore. In the evening along came the zookeeper with the food. He brought them fish, fruit and maize and each ate what they liked best. The bears really enjoyed their food and they suddenly began to laugh about their quarrel, so they made it up and became better friends than they had been before.

18th February

The Carnival

How exciting is the Carnival,
With Micky Mouse and fellows tail!
Stuck in the middle of my bed,
Books and pens and needle and thread,
There's records to break if I move my leg,
I want to move but there's nowhere to tread!
But Carnival's coming, I must have a costume,
A Wizard I'll be when I next clean my room!
How exciting is the Carnival,
With Micky Mouse and fellows tall!

19th February

Susan and Pipsi (1)

Hannah's little doll used to be wonderful, but she'd played with her so much she was worn out, and now Hannah didn't

Susan and Pipsi (2)

Pipsi laid the doll down on the floor and said to her: "Can you forgive me? It poured with rain today and I forget I had left you outside." He took Susan dripping wet into his kennel and he stayed awake to make sure she did not catch pneumonia.

The next day Pipsi took Susan to his little wife. "Oh, how ill she looks!" said the poodle. So she washed her completely in a hot bubble-bath and you could hardly recognise her. Then she took her to the dolly doctor who gave her new sandals, socks and a little dress and umbrella to match. She looked like a new doll. Hannah didn't know anything about it and, because it would soon be her birthday, the new Susan was to be her surprise. But Hannah didn't want any presents, she just wanted her old doll back. When she saw her standing there on her birthday, she exclaimed: "Oh Susan, how beautiful you are, I hardly recognised you. Oh, my dear, dear doll. How badly I treated you! Forgive me, I really love you very much!"

like her anymore. But her poodle Pipsi still loved Susan the little doll and always took her for walks. One day, when Hannah had some pocket-money to spend, they went to town to look in the toy shops. So many toys! In one shop she saw a really beautiful doll. "Oh, I wish she was mine", sighed Hannah. She didn't think about Susan, how she was lying there neglected on the floor with a torn dress and without her shoes. All she had to do was sew her a new dress and she would be as good as new.

When it was bedtime, Hannah got washed, combed her hair and went to bed. She didn't spare a thought for Susan. When she was asleep, the other toys began to talk. They were worried about Susan, because they hadn't seen her for such a long time. Just as they were about to look for her, in walked Pipsi, carrying the doll.

The Yellow Flower (1)

There was once a very good and rich King, who was loved dearly by all his subjects. So he should have been a very happy man. But he suffered from a stupid

illness: after every sentence he had to sneeze, and not even the most famous doctors could make him better. One day along came an old woman who insisted on seeing the King. Eventually she was given permission, and she told the King of a yellow flower that could heal him of his illness.

The old woman said, "The flower grows a long way from here, behind the thirteenth mountain, and only a pair of twins will ever find it." Immediately the King sent out an order to find a pair of clever twins. So Karl and Kathy were chosen, because they were the cleverest. The children set off straight away. When they had passed the first mountain they came to a beautiful meadow. There they met a wolf, who wanted to lead them from their path.

But they'd heard of Little Red Riding Hood and knew you should never trust wolves. So they went on. Not long after that they met a big bear who introduced himself as the bear who had been cursed and then afterwards had married Snow White. Since it was getting dark, the two children stayed in the bear's warm cave.

22nd February

The Yellow Flower (2)

The next day Karl and Kathy set off again. Just as they were getting thirsty they met an old farmer's wife, who was carrying a basket of big juicy red apples. Karl said, "That's certainly Snow White's wicked stepmother!" And, despite their thirst,

they didn't take an apple. In the evening they reached the seventh mountain where the seven dwarfs lived, who welcomed them heartily. Towards midday the next day they walked over the thirteenth mountain. There, in a big orchard, they saw a big tree with the most beautiful apples. It called out, "Shake me, all my apples are ripe!" The two children quickly picked all the apples. Straight away, the old woman who had told the King about the yellow flower appeared. She called over a stork who carried the children home on its back. Soon, in the distance, they saw the tower of their home town. After they had landed in the palace yard the children were brought to the King in triumph. When the King smelled the flower, he sneezed for the very last time.

35

23rd February

Lisa and Lena (1)

Lisa and Lena take the train,
Their holiday weather brings no rain,
They're going to the Island Ness,
But these children know no thankfulness!

Poor old Aunty has a bath,
When they hear a crash they laugh,
The naughty children greased the floor,
And stand there grinning at the door.

On Aunty who invited them,
They play their tricks again and again.
Just look how they stick out their
tongues,
But they don't care, they're having fun.

24th February

Lisa and Lena (2)

So now today poor Aunt is ill,
But they just cry, "Oh what a thrill!"
While on the beach they pick some
thistles,
At the thought of mischief they gaily
whistle.

And where do they the thistles hide?
Under the bedclothes of the maid!
And when she jumps up full of pain,
The girls run away and laugh again.

In some flowers they plant a lobster,
They take them to Aunt and give them to her.
Aunt thinks their jokes are at an end,
And gives them both some money to spend.

25th February

Lisa and Lena (3)

When alone she sniffs the rose,
The lobster grabs her by the nose,
And if the doctor hadn't come,
I'm afraid her life would have been done.

Lisa and Lena (4)

Lena nudged Lisa, "Look, there's a man,
While he's asleep, let's bury him with sand."
So, 1, 2, 3, the work was done,
And giggling then away they ran.

And as he slept, the sea came home,
But the poor old man just couldn't move,
Then out came the brave sea-watch brigade,
And thanks to them the man was saved.

Lisa and Lena (5)

Then to the water wading in,
Came a woman in a rubber ring.
They tied it up and when she saw,
With fear she sank down in the sea.

"Water, water, please don't drown me,"
But the cold North sea it had no pity.
The life-savers saw her and then came running,
But Lisa and Lena just swam off grinning.

Lisa and Lena (6)

On the sixth day came the carnival,
In funny costumes one and all,
Ran the children over the dunes,
While Lisa and Lena bought balloons.

And both their hearts with mischief full,
They ran and sang over sand and hill,

While Lisa orders their ice-cream,
Lena finds a rusty nail.

The friendly dog they beckon over,
And fix the balloons onto its collar.

The dog he cried as he's raised to the sky,
And his mistress can't do else but cry.

Lisa and Lena (7)

Because the holidays are nearly out,
Lisa and Lena hire a boat.
While naughty thoughts in their heads do form,
Up rise the waves and here comes a storm.

So now they shout, but cannot win,
For neither naughty girls can swim.
And though they cry to be set free,
Only a whale has heard their plea.

Next day a fisherman did see,
A whale near the isle of Ness-on-sea
Young and old to the spot they ran,
To see the enormous animal.

A harpoon was cast which caught the thing,
But guess what there was found within!
The remains of the two girls found together,
Which were sadly taken and placed in a meadow.

Of Lisa, a hat, a ribbon, a plait,
Of Lena her shoes and her dress squashed flat,
From the two girls their lives had flown,
And only by these things were they known.

1st March

The Dear Little Sunny Ray

Bright flowers blooming,
Happy children running,
Picking flowers for mummy,
Now the weather's sunny.
See how little sunny ray,
Has melted all the ice away.

2nd March

A happy birthday

It's Nina's birthday! She wanted a white mouse, and she got one. Of course she's very pleased.
In the afternoon come Susi, Dawn, Jane and Michael. They have coffee and cakes.

Afterwards the children play with the mouse. The mouse crawls up to Nina's shoulder and turns around on Jane's finger. Then the children play this game. Nina's mum secretly puts five things on a tray: an apple, a little car, a piece of chewing-gum, a building brick and a pen. The children are allowed to look at them and then they're covered with a cloth. Everyone's given a pad and each has to draw what they've seen. Susie can't remember the pen, and Jane totally forgets the brick. Only Michael remembers them all and he gets a prize. The children want to play again. This time on the tray is a rolling-pin, a key, a piece of cheese and a book. The tray is covered again. While the children are drawing, suddenly the cloth moves. Nina jumps up and carefully lifts a corner of the cloth. Out runs the startled mouse! She's eaten the cheese because mice love cheese!

3rd March

The Swineherd (I)

Once there was a poor Prince. He had a kingdom, but only a very small one. Even so, there were hundreds of Princesses who would have married him. But he was in love with the Kaiser's daughter, and she was very proud and vain.

The Prince decided to send her a present. He went to his father's grave where a beautiful rose tree grew, which only bloomed every five years. In the tree there lived a nightingale who sang the most beautiful melodies you can imagine. He sent these presents to the Princess. When the Princess saw the rose, she clapped her hands for joy, but

when she touched it she burst out crying. "It's a real rose," she exclaimed. Then she saw the nightingale, which sang so beautifully that all the ladies-in-waiting called out, "Superbe! Charmant!" (They could all speak French, each one worse than the other.) The Kaiser was also delighted, but the Princess wanted an artificial bird, and let the bird fly away because it was real.

The Swineherd (2)

When the Prince heard that the Princess had refused his gifts, he didn't let himself

get downhearted. He took a jar of brown paint and coloured his face with it. Then he put on old clothes and went to the Kaiser's palace. The post of Swineherd had become vacant in the palace, and so the Prince took on the job.

The Prince was given a dirty little cabin down by the pig stalls. He was never bored. He had brought some tools with him and he set to work straight away. By evening he had made a little saucepan with bells on. As soon as the saucepan was boiling, it sang beautifully, and sang the tune, "Oh my darling Clementine!" That was much better than a rose! The next day he made an instrument with strings that sounded wonderful. The Prince kept everything in his house and went about his work.

he Swineherd (3)

)ne day the Princess came by with her
adies-in-waiting, just as the Prince was
rying out the new instrument. "I've
iever heard anything so beautiful. Go

The next day when the Princess was
again walking by the pig stall, she heard
the tune, "Oh my darling Clementine!"
That was her favourite tune. When she
went into the hut and saw the saucepan
of bells, she just had to have it.

"What do you want for it?" she asked.

"A hundred kisses from the Princess,"
demanded the Swineherd.

The Princess started kissing, and the
ladies-in-waiting were too busy counting
to notice the Kaiser coming. When the
Kaiser saw his daughter kissing the
Swineherd, he was very angry, and both
of them were banished from his,
Kingdom.

The Princess cried bitterly. "Oh, woe is
me!" she wailed. "If only I'd accepted the
handsome Prince. Now I've got to spend
the rest of my life with a Swineherd!" The
Swineherd went behind a tree, wiped the
paint from his face, and put on his
Prince's garb which he had hidden there.
He said to her: "I've learned to despise
you! You didn't want me, but you kissed
a Swineherd for a game! Now you've got
what you deserve!" He went back to his
kingdom and closed the gates behind
him, and still the Princess stands there
and sings, "Oh my darling Clementine."

nd find out how much the instrument
osts!" she said. "He wants ten kisses
rom the Princess!" said the lady in
vaiting when she came back. So the
adies had to stand in front of the Princess
o that no one could see her kissing the
wineherd. When the Princess had her
nstrument, the whole palace rang with
s beautiful music.

The Bird-wedding (I)

On a lovely sunny day,
Mr Blackbird calls, "It's my
wedding day!"

Mrs. Thrush arrives with a wedding-gift,
This custom one must never miss!

The wagtail is my blushing bride,
Won't she look lovely by my side!"

The finch for the bride has brought some
flowers,
To get the best he's searched for hours.

The Bird-wedding (2)

In church the nightingale brightly sings,
While the choir-birds flap time with their
wings.

The owl there has a clever head,
He tucks into the lovely spread.

The raven's speech is moving to hear,
And some of the birds look on in tears.

At midnight when the feat is done,
The greenfinch lights them gaily home!

8th March

Barbara in the Department Store

Today Barbara is allowed to go shopping with her mother in the big department store. She likes going on the moving-staircase best of all. You just have to step quickly onto the lowest stair and then you have to wait until this stair reaches the top. She likes it so much that she runs off and goes all over the shop on the escalator until she gets to the toy department. There she forgets the escalator completely. She goes from one shelf to another – and then she suddenly remembers mummy. How can she find mummy again? She gets very frightened and starts to cry.

"Why are you crying?" asks a young shop assistant.

"I've lost my mummy," sobs Barbara.

Shortly afterwards the loudspeaker announces that they have found little Barbara who is looking for her mummy. Her mother hears this, and full of relief she takes the moving staircase up to the toy department. Barbara runs towards her, sobbing, and throws her arms around her: "Mummy, I'm so glad you're there, and I promise I'll never run off again."

9th March

Flower-Peter (I)

Peter and Karl had just got out of school and were full of energy. "Let's play Indians," called Peter. But the enemy Indian trail led through the flowers on the meadow. How the flowers' heads flew as they chopped them with their sticks! Doris, Peter's little sister cried bitterly as she came to her favourite rose tree and found it so wildly and cruelly destroyed.

Next day the two boys wanted to play at Knights. Peter was just building a stone wall in a ring when it occurred to him that the inside should be soft, so he sent Karl into the wood where there was some soft heather. Meanwhile Peter was crushing countless flowers with the heavy stones, but what did that matter to him? Suddenly a little man stood before him with a flower-covered hat and staff. It was the flower pixie. He said to Peter: "Now you will pay for the flower souls you have laid to waste. You will now become a flower so that you'll understand the pain that little flowers suffer." Then Peter noticed himself getting smaller and smaller, until he stood there as a flower in the field.

10th March

Flower-Peter (2)

Karl came back with loads of heather from the wood. When he reached the Knights' castle, he found only Peter's schoolbag. He called Peter's name a few times, but then he took his schoolbag and started home. Peter wanted to call out, but he couldn't speak anymore. Karl came towards the flower and Peter shook with fear as he saw the huge shoes over him. Karl trod on him and Peter was overcome with pain. Karl went out of sight and the Bluebell felt very lonely and unhappy. After a while he began to feel thirsty, for the crushed stem couldn't draw any water from the ground. Thankfully, along came little Doris, who picked up the crushed flower. Full of pity for it she picked it up and took it home with her. How glad Peter was when he saw his sister's dear face. Doris put the flower in a pretty red vase. After a while along came Karl. He was astonished that

Peter wasn't at home. Peter's parents got very anxious that their son had disappeared. They went out to look for him, but he was nowhere to be seen. All that night Doris tossed and turned until she suddenly got up and ran out of the house and down to the big meadow where the flower pixie lived. She knew him because she was the flowers' best friend.

Crying, she sat down among her flower friends and poured out her heart. Then behind her appeared the flower pixie. The pixie relented, for even the flowers were crying for naughty Peter, and he promised to free Peter from his spell.

Relieved, Doris went home and fell asleep straight away. Peter had seen her rush out, but he hung his head in sorrow because he knew nothing of the conversation with the flower pixie. However, he had a glimmer of hope because he knew his sister would try to help him.

Flower-Peter (3)

When it struck midnight a beautiful scent of roses streamed through the house, and the flower-pixie appeared. He had brought his staff with him and when he touched the bluebell with it, his leaves began to grow and soon he was a real boy again. Happily Peter looked around him. The vase he had stood in was broken. Sudenly a voice spoke to him and as he looked around, he recognised the flower-pixie. "I have forgiven you," said the pixie, "You have learned for yourself that even the smallest flower can feel pain. Before I go you are to promise me something. You are to tell all children about your experience, and about the quiet life of the flower." Peter shook the

pixies hand and promised; then the pixie disappeared just as he had come. Ever since then Peter has never mistreated a flower and he told his story to every child he knew. But when he got older, he noticed he didn't know as many children anymore, so he sat down and wrote his story, so that children all over the world would know.

12th March

Where have I been?

"Where have I been, give me a clue!"
"Then let me take a look at you.
Well, spiders' webs stick to your clothes,
The scent of pine on hands and toes,
To the pine wood you have been,
By all the forest creatures seen.

Beneath the trees you linger there,
Pine needles drop, cling to your hair."
"What else did I do there by chance?"
"Well I can tell you at a glance.
Blue stains around your mouth so merry,
Can only mean you've had blackberry!"

13th March

The birthday present

When John woke up, the sun was already shining into the room. Everything was still and quiet. Suddenly the little boy sat up in bed. Of course! It was his birthday! Quickly John slipped out of bed – Mummy had hidden his presents somewhere like she always did. John ran through the room but he couldn't find anything. Maybe in the garden? He heard a noise at the front door and quickly looked out. There sat a kitten on the mat, purring softly. John tenderly took him in his arms and ran, overjoyed, to his parents.

"Mummy, Daddy, thank you so much! I've never had such a beautiful present!" he cried. His parents looked at him in surprise. The kitten wasn't from them! They had bought the roller-skates for him that he had wanted for so long. They were underneath the apple tree in the garden. But where did the kitten come from? He must have put himself in front of the door as a surprise present for John.

14th March

Rumpelstiltskin (I)

There was once a miller who was very poor, but he had a beautiful daughter. Now it happened that one day the King spoke to him. Trying to impress him the miller said, "I have a daughter who can spin straw into gold." The King was greedy for gold, so he told the miller to

bring his daughter to his castle the next day. Now, when the girl was brought to him, he led her into a chamber that was full of straw. He gave her a spinning wheel and said, "If the straw hasn't been spun to gold by morning, I'll have your head!" Then he left her alone. Now the poor miller's daughter sat down and didn't know what to do, for she had no

idea how to spin straw into gold. Then, suddenly, the door opened, and in came a little man. "What will you give me if I spin this straw into gold for you? he asked. "I'll give you my necklace!" said the girl. The little man sat down in front of the spinning wheel, and soon the spool was full of gold! He worked all night until all the straw had been spun, and all the

spools were full of gold. At sunrise the King came. When he saw the gold he was astonished and overjoyed, but his heart became even more greedy for gold.

15th March

Rumpelstiltskin (2)

The King took the miller's daughter into a much bigger chamber full of straw and ordered her to spin it that night if she valued her life. Again the door opened and the little man appeared. "What will you give me this time if I spin the straw into gold?" he asked her. "The ring from my finger," said the girl. The little man greedily grabbed the ring and by morning all the straw had been spun. The King was overjoyed, but he still wasn't satisfied. He took the girl into an even bigger room and said. "If you spin all that into gold, I'll make you my wife!" And again, when the girl was alone, the little man came and said, "What will you give me this time if I spin the straw?" "I have nothing left!" answered the girl sadly. "Then promise me your first child," demanded the little man. In her desperation the girl promised, and the little man again spun all the straw into gold. When the King came the next day and found the gold, he married the girl, and so she was Queen!

16th March

Rumpelstiltskin (3)

After a year, the Queen had a child, but she had forgotten about the little man. One day, however, he burst into the chamber and said, "Now give me what you promised!" The Queen was terrified and began to cry bitterly. The little man felt sorry for her and said, "I'll give you three days to learn my name. If you do, then you can keep your child." When he had gone, the Queen tried to think of all the names under the sun; she even sent out a messenger to find out new names. The next day, when the little man came back, she began with Casper, Melchior, Balthasar, and ended with the last name she knew. But after every name, the man said, "That's not my name!" On the

second day she asked around the neighbourhood for the most unusual names. "Are you perhaps called Rippenbiest, or Hammelswade, or Shruppelshrop?" But to every name he answered with glee, "That's not my name!" The next day the messenger came back. He said, "I couldn't find any new names, but when I came to the top of a mountain, I saw a little man dancing in front of a fire singing:
"Tonight I'll dance, tonight I'll sing,
Tomorrow I'll fetch the son of the King.
What fun, what a game,
Rumpelstiltskin is my name!"
The Queen rewarded the messenger so well that he would never have to work

again! Soon afterwards the little man came in. The Queen started listing many

51

names, and right at the end she said, "Are you called Rumpelstiltskin?" The little man turned red with anger and stamped his foot so hard he broke the floorboards! He ran angrily out of the castle and was never seen again. Meanwhile the King's heart had grown softer and he was no longer greedy for gold. The son grew into a fine young man, and they all lived happily ever after.

17th March

The Little Raindrops (1)

it flies right up. They can already hear the raindrops falling on the leaves and they put their coats over their heads. From the edge of the forest comes a friendly deer who takes them to his house, made of leaves, for shelter. There they sit listening to the rain, pattering on the leaves.

Terry and Una went to visit grandma today, and she was so pleased to see them. Now they're off again and they turn back to wave goodbye. On the way home they pick some flowers for their mother from the meadow. Suddenly a black cloud hovers over them and the wind begins to blow Una's dress so hard

18th March

The Little Raindrops (2)

They sit looking at the field and see two little rabbits who in spite of the thunder and lightening bound around full of energy. In wanders a little calf who is

Just look how happy the farmer's wife is at having back her calf. She was so pleased that she gave the children a basket full of sausages and eggs. How pleased their mother would be! They ran home to have them for tea.

frightened by the thunder. It stands there soaked through by the rain and can hardly move for fear. The rabbits who till now have been so brave, hop quickly away, for the shy calf is like a giant to them. Still frightened, the little calf sniffs Una's flowers and then sits down at her feet. Gradually it gets brighter and the clouds rush past. A wonderful rainbow has soaked up all the rain, and the sun spreads out all over the sky. Along comes the farmer to catch his calf, and the calf happily jumps up and follows him home.

19th March

Simbo the Little Lion (1)

Simbo the little lion and the little monkey Jojo are sitting under a tree in the jungle. From a nearby tree the parrot Lorax squawks,

"You should have seen me in the circus! I was a sensation!"

"I'd like to be in a circus," sighs Simbo.

"Then you'd better hurry," says Lorax, "For soon the circus people are coming to look for animals."

From then on Simbo and Jojo practise every day. They try somersaulting from trees, and juggling with coconuts, but the parrot thinks they ought to try something different, because all that is already done. Simbo is sad, but Jojo says, "You should try tightrope walking, for a lion's never done that before."

So Simbo climbs a tree and wobbles on the swaying branch. *Flop!* he falls down with a crash.

20th March

Simbo the Little Lion (2)

One day there was great excitement in the jungle – the circus people were coming! Along comes the Circus-master who says to his assistant Flippo, "We need a completely new act, a real sensation, as not many people have been coming to the circus recently."

"That's why lions don't walk tightropes!" squawks Lorax.

Flippo points to a giraffe who is making a knot in his neck. "Excellent, I must say, but we need a sensation!" says the Circus-master. Then Simbo and Jojo jump onto the rope and perform the wonderful tricks they have practiced. The Circus-master cried, "I say! How excellent! That's a real sensation!"

Then Simbo and Jojo have to go straight to the Circus and the other animals are quite envious, because they have to stay in the jungle.

Before long Simbo is famous and many people come to see him. Now the tent is always full and there wouldn't even be room for a mouse!

21st March

Four short stories

Once there sat an old owl shouting out words of wisdom. Then along came a Lirumlarumplatypus who kicked him with his flat foot.

"Hey!" hooted the owl, "Why did you kick me? Can't I sit here and shout out my words of wisdom?"

There was once an old farmer and an old mule. The farmer sat in one corner and the mule sat in the other corner, and the farmer looked at the mule and the mule looked at the farmer.

There was once a farmer who searched through his house. He found nothing but a mouse with a stumpy tail. If the mouse had had a longer tail, my story would have been longer.

"Boy, what are you doing there?"
"Quiet father, I'm catching mice!"
"Have you caught any yet?"
"Yes, father, when I have this one on the fishing rod and then another, then I'll have two!"

Tom Thumb (1)

Once there lived a poor farmer and his wife, who both really wanted a child. "Even if he was no bigger than my thumb!" sighed the woman. In fact, after seven months, the woman had a child who was no bigger than her thumb, and so she called him Tom Thumb. Tom Thumb was clever, and when one day his father had to go into the wood, Tom Thumb promised to bring the waggon later. When the time came, his mother harnessed the horse and placed Tom Thumb in its ear. The little boy shouted out the directions to the horse and the horse sped off. Then two men came along and stood looking at the horse in amazement, since someone was obviously directing the horse, but there was no one to be seen. Curiously the men followed the cart, and when they saw Tom Thumb, they were dumbstruck. They said to the farmer, "Sell us the little man and we'll take good care of him."
At first Tom's father wouldn't hear of it, but Tom knew how to persuade him. "I'll soon come back," he said. They gave Tom's father a fine piece of gold, put him in one of their hats and took him away.

Tom Thumb (2)

When it got dark, Tom Thumb asked to be put down, and the men put him down in the field. Tom then hid himself in a mouse's burrow. The men searched for him for a while, but then angrily went away. Then Tom was tired, so he climbed into a snail's shell and went to sleep. Before long, however, two thieves talking together woke him up. They were talking about stealing the priest's gold. "How

shall we do it?'' said the thieves. ''I know!'' said Tom Thumb jumping out of his shell, ''Take me with you and I'll help you!'' So the thieves took him along. It was easy for Tom to get into the chamber because he was so small. As soon as he stood there among the gold, he cried out at the top of his voice, ''Do you want to take everything?'' He shouted so loud he woke the cook, so the thieves ran away. Tom Thumb climbed out through the grate, and went to sleep in a hay loft.

24th March

Tom Thumb (3)

The next day Tom Thumb wanted to go home, but he wanted to do other things first. The farm hand came and took an armful of hay for the cow, but he took the hay in which Tom Thumb was sleeping. Before Tom knew what was happening, he had landed in the stomach of a cow. The more hay the cow ate, the more cramped it became for Tom, so he cried out, ''Don't bring me anymore to eat!'' The farm hand was so terrified to hear a cow talk that she knocked over a bucket of milk, and ran to the priest. The priest thought there must be an evil spirit in the cow and he had it killed. The stomach in which Tom sat was thrown into the manure heap. Along came a hungry wolf, who swallowed the whole stomach with

one bite, but the wolf was still hungry, so Tom Thumb described to him where he could get ham and sausages. But crafty little Tom Thumb had directed him to his own house. When the wolf had got into the kitchen and eaten as much as he could, he was too fat to go back the way he had come. Little Tom Thumb began to shout as loudly as he could, and finally his mother and father woke up. They ran to the larder, and through the keyhole they saw the wolf, and from the stomach of the wolf they could hear their son's voice. They killed the wolf, cut his stomach open very carefully, and out jumped Tom Thumb. How happy they were to be together again!

25th March

The Little Sandman

With sack in hand, he sees our house,
And enters quiet as a mouse.
Unseen, upon the stairs he treads,
While all are tucked up in their beds.
He tiptoes softly in the door,
His footsteps muffled on the floor.
He scatters sand dust, as he means,
To take us to the land of dreams.
Our eyes are filled with his sweet dust,
To him our precious sleep we trust.
When day is near he slips away,
What is his name?
I cannot say.

26th March

The Hen Who Didn't Want to Lay Eggs

The little hen lived on a big farm, with many other hens. There they all ate corn and laid lots of eggs, in the evening they all settled down in a comfortable hen-stall and went to sleep until morning. One day the little hen got bored, and went on a journey to meet more people. On the way she met a duck who invited her to go swimming, but the little hen couldn't swim. Later she met a cat who asked her to go mouse-hunting with him, but the hen didn't like mice. *"Woof, woof!"*

Suddenly there stood a big dog. "I've buried a bone!" he said, "Come with me, you can help me eat it!" But the little hen didn't like bones either, she preferred corn. "No one understands me," sighed the little hen. "I'm going home again where I belong!"

27th March

Pussel and the Moonlight (1)

When the sun goes down, the moon spreads its magic white light over the land, but some people can't bear it! Birds duck down in their nests, all the hens go to sleep, and the dogs start to howl.

When it's dark, Pussel listens and is very excited. He's going to escape into the night where no one can see him! He creeps through the garden and out through the fence. He glides through the village to have a proper look at the moon.

he cries. But what's that sniffing along – a wolf?! Something pushes him over and starts licking his face – it's the next-door neighbour's dog. The dog leads him home, but his eyes are almost as heavy as his feet. Then two warm arms embrace him, and he sees his dear mother's face!

A deer ventures out of its leafy house, and Pussel can hardly believe it – every tree has a face!
And who's sitting up there in the tree? Big eyes are staring at him! He's never seen anything stare like that!

Pussel and the Moonlight (2)

Pussel runs to the meadow, to which the moon has lit up a bright path. He springs along and *splash!* he falls into the stream!
Pussel desperately grabs at the reeds and drags himself out of the water. "I wish I was at home!" he sobs. He races past bushes and sees the moor stretching out before him, "I don't know where I am!"

The Easter Rabbits (1)

Winter, the stormy giant, had to go back north when Spring came. But he didn't want to hand over the field to his enemy without a fight, so he made the north wind blow through the land. On a flower-covered meadow he found a flower elf.

He grabbed the elf and took her to Winter. Shivering with cold, she stood before the icy giant. ''At last a child of my enemy is in my power. If you change my Kingdom into a gaily-coloured meadow, I will gladly give you your freedom.'' The little elf touched the frozen ground and tears came to her eyes. ''It's impossible,'' she said. So from then on she had to stay in Winter's palace and play with the snowdrops. But one day she said to Winter, ''Please let me out onto the meadow one more time! I will ask the flowers to follow me into your Kingdom,'' Winter gave her just one hour. The north wind carried her back to Spring's Kingdom. All the flowers and animals were overjoyed to see her again.

The Easter Rabbits (2)

The elf was happy to be in Spring's Kingdom again, but how the hour was flying by! She asked the flowers and animals to help her.

"We can't follow you," said the flowers, "The icy breath of Winter would kill us." Finally, an old wise rabbit said, "We rabbits can help you! On Easter Sunday, when the sun rises, Winter's Kingdom will look like a Spring meadow!" When the elf had gone, the rabbit ordered the others to go and get some eggs. All the rabbits ran into the villages and asked the hens for eggs, and the hens were only too pleased to give them. Proudly the rabbits came back and spread the eggs out on the meadow. "Now it's your turn to help, flowers!" said the old rabbit. "Colour the eggs so brightly that Winter will think they are flowers."

On Easter morning, the rabbits slipped into Winter's Kingdom, and spread them out on the meadow. When Winter got up in the morning, he couldn't believe his eyes. Had the elf done that! Winter gave the elf her freedom. Later, however, he realised he had been tricked, but the love of the rabbits and flowers for the elf had moved him so much that never again did he steal a child of Spring.

Why the Rabbit Brings Easter

Many hundreds of years ago, when animals lived happily together, there lived a monkey, a fox, an otter and a rabbit. One day the otter ran to the river to get something to eat. There he saw seven fish in the sand. A fisherman must have lost them, so he called several times. But when no one called back, he took the fish for himself. The fox was looking for food in the empty hut of a wood-cutter. He found a few pieces of bread and called out to see if they belonged to anyone. But no one called back, so he took them for himself.

The monkey went up a banana tree to get some fruit. At this moment, God looked down onto the Earth to see if his creatures were ready to help someone in need. He dressed himself up as a tramp and went down to the river. There he found the otter. The otter saw that the tramp was hungry and invited him to share his food, but the tramp took nothing, went away and said he would come back. Then the tramp went to the fox and the monkey, and the same thing happened. When he came to the rabbit, the rabbit said, "Unfortunately I only eat grass. That's not good enough for you, so eat me instead!" God was so moved that he said to the rabbit, "From now on you are to bring luck among men. You are to bring Easter eggs to them, to show that everything will bring new life and rise again." So the rabbit set to work!

The Dear Little Sunny Ray

The sunny ray melts Snowman's nose,
And water trickles to his toes!
The newly blossomed trees do sway
And winter has to go away,
The changing moods of April's face,
Lead us all a merry chase!

2nd April

Peter's Restless Night

"But, Peter," said Mummy. "Are you just going to leave your toys over the floor all night? Put them away before you go to bed." But Peter didn't clear up, he was so tired. "You just wait," said mummy. These were the last words he heard before going to sleep . . . During the night, Peter was woken up by a loud din. The fire-engine was zooming across the room. Behind it raced the police car. "Ouch!" cried Teddy. "The fire engine just ran over my foot." But when the cars ran over his nice picture book, Peter got angry. "Mummy is right. From now on I'm going to clear my toys away before I go to bed." Suddenly everything is quiet and it's broad daylight. Did he dream it all?

3rd April

The Musicians of Bremen (1)

Once upon a time, a man had a donkey, who had worked hard and well for many a year. Now he was old, he was no longer fit for his work and his master wanted to get rid of him.

Soon they came to a brightly-lit robbers' house. The donkey, who was the biggest, looked in through the window, and the other animals climbed on his back. There they saw a table decked with food and drink. "I wish we were in there," thought the animals. Then the animals thought of a way to chase the robbers out. Sitting on each others' backs, they all started to sing. The donkey hee-hawed, the dog barked, the cat miaowed and the cock crowed. Then they knocked against the window so that it broke.

The robbers jumped out of their skins, because they thought it was a ghost, and they fled into the wood. The animals were overjoyed that their plan had succeeded.

But the donkey found out and ran away to Bremen. There he wanted to become the town musician. He came upon a hound dog, who had also run away from home.

The donkey persuaded him to go along with him. Before long they met a cat who was tired of catching mice, and because of this, his mistress had tried to drown him. The donkey said, "Come with us to Bremen, you're good at night music!" Then they met a cock, who was crowing with fear because he was going to be made into soup the next day. "You've got a good voice," said the donkey, and they persuaded him to go along too.

4th April

The musicians of Bremen (2)

The animals stayed overnight in the wood. The donkey and the dog slept under a tree, the cat slept in the branches and the cock flew to the very top. There he saw a light shining in the distance, so they all got up and went towards it.

The Musicians of Bremen (3)

scratched him. He was terrified and wanted to run out of the door, but the dog was sleeping there and bit him on the leg. As he was running past the manure heap, the donkey gave him a kick with his hind leg, and the cock, woken up by the din, crowed *"Kikeriki".* The man ran as fast as he could back to his leader. He reported to him: "In the house sits a terrible witch. As I was trying to light a candle, she sprang at me and scratched me with her long nails. Then when I tried to run out of the door, there stood a man

After our four musicians had chased the robbers away, they sat down at the table and ate as though they had not eaten for a week. When they had finished, they put out the light, and each found a comfortable place to sleep.

When it was after midnight, and from far away the robbers could see that there was no light burning anymore, the leader said, "We shouldn't have let ourselves be chased away like that!" And he said that someone ought to go and check the house.

The man who was sent found everything quiet. He went into the kitchen to light a fire. Because he took the cat's fiery eyes for burning coal, he poked it with a poker to make a better fire. But the cat didn't like that, and sprang at his face, bit him and

with a knife, and he stabbed me with it in my leg. In the yard waits a huge monster who hit me with a big wooded club so that I lost all sight and hearing, Up on the roof sat the judge who called down 'Bring the rascal to me,' then I ran away as fast as I could.''

From then on the robbers never returned to the house, but the four musicians like it so much they don't want to leave.''

In April

Look, children, how April has his way!
Sunshine and rain all in one day!
Clouds and then blue skies, snowflakes too,
Mischievous wind is chasing you.

Just when you think the day is fine,
And in the fields you'd like to dine,
Along comes April at his worst
And sends along a new cloudburst.

The Story About the Sausage

Once again it was the annual market, and all the children were excited. Only little Michael wasn't happy. He had lost the money that mummy had given him. Now he was standing before the sausage stand, longing for one of those enormous sausages that were hanging there. Two girls who were standing there with their sausages took pity on him and said ''Here, little man, if you're so hungry you can have one of ours.'' And they gave him a sausage. Because he was so pleased, Michael forgot to say thank you.

But what was that up there? A balloon with a funny face and a big red nose was floating in the air. Michael stood looking at him and the sausage slipped off his plate onto the floor. Quick as a flash the cat Felix whipped it up and ran away with it. The cat stopped behind a wall and licked his lips. Suddenly he heard a "woof" and he jumped onto the roof in fear. The dog snapped up the sausage and ran away. But he didn't get far. Soon he met a bigger dog who also wanted the sausage. The big dog barked at the little

Gaily the monkey looked down, but then along came a stork and he quickly had the sausage in his beak. He flew over the houses to his nest. That would be a fine meal for his little children. But then a big face with a big red nose appeared over the nest! The stork was terrified, and tried to push the thing away with his beak, and of course the sausage fell out. It had, of course, been the balloon again. The sausage fell and fell, until it fell into a chimney. The sausage stayed there until one day the chimney-sweeper pulled it down. The lady of the house put the sausage in the bin, and there it would have stayed if father mouse had not gone for his daily walk to the bin, where he sometimes found the most delightful things to eat that the humans had thrown away.

Father mouse's little eyes grew bigger and bigger. A real sausage! He hurried back home to fetch his family, because he couldn't drag the sausage on his own. Oh what a feast! After they had sniffed and wondered over the sausage, they sat down at the table and they all ate as much as they could. Afterwards they all had to have a rest, but they often talk about their enormous sausage!

dog, but the little dog was brave and barked back. Then the sausage fell from his mouth and soon the bigger dog had it in his mouth. The little dog looked at him sadly.

The big dog ran to his waggon, for he was a watchdog for the market. But a funny little monkey called Jojo lived there too. He was always up to tricks. Scarcely had the dog put the sausage down when he pulled him by the tail. When the dog turned round, Jojo had taken the sausage and had climbed onto some scaffolding.

Munchhouse's Adventure –
a Visit to the Moon

In spite of all my caution, I was taken prisoner in Turkey and was sold into slavery. There I had to take care of the sultan's bees. Once two bears stole a bee and I threw my axe at them. They ran

away, but my axe flew higher and higher and landed on the moon. With a fast-growing beanstalk I made myself a rope and managed to reach the moon. After some searching I found my axe.

The Water Nymph

A brother and sister were playing together by a well. Absorbed in their game they suddenly fell in. Down below was a water nymph who said to them: "At least I have someone to work for me. But you'd better work hard!" To the girl she gave flax to spin and she also had to carry water in a barrel. The boy had to fell trees with a blunt axe. With all this work they never got anything to eat. The children tried to think of a way to escape, and one day when they went to church they ran away. When the nymph saw they had disappeared she raced after them, but the children saw her from a distance. The girl threw a big bush behind her, which grew into a huge bush mountain with thousands of thistles. But although she had great difficulty, the nymph climbed over it. Then the boy threw a comb behind him, and there grew a big comb mountain with thousands of spikes. But again the nymph climbed over. Then the girl threw a mirror, which grew into a big mirror mountain, which was so slippy the nymph couldn't climb over. The nymph was furious, and rushed home to fetch her axe. She struck at the mirror with her axe, but it took her so long to get through that the children had got too far away for her to catch them. The nymph had never been so angry in her life. There was nothing left for her to do but return to her well. But the children were so happy to be free again that they flung their arms round each other and swore never to be so careless again.

When the children got home their parents were happy again.

10th April

Little Children

Little Children, go to bed,
Lay gently down your weary head,
With bedclothes well tucked-in around,
Now in peaceful sleep abound.
When morning comes then wake and say,
"Here starts another sunny day."

11th April

The Flying Trunk (1)

Once upon a time there was a businessman who was so rich that he could have paved all the streets with silver. Of course he didn't because he was a wise man. But all the best people have to die and he died too. His son inherited most of his wealth, but he was a careless man. Every night he was at a ball, he made paper dragons out of notes, and spun golden coins instead of stones on water. Soon all he had left was a pair of pyjamas and some trousers.

But when his money had gone, he also lost his friends, except one.   This friend gave him an old trunk to put all his belongings in, but since he didn't have any he put himself in. But when he touched the lock, the trunk flew off into the sky, and it flew so far that it came to Turkey. He hid the trunk in the middle of a forest and went into town.

He caught sight of a castle on a mountain, and when he met a woman with her little child he asked about it.

"There lives the Sultan's daughter," she said, "A fortune-teller told her that her heart would one day be broken by a lover. So now she can only have a visit if the Sultan and his wife are there." On hearing this the son went back to his trunk and flew up to the castle. He landed on the roof and crept in through the window of the Princess's bedroom.

The Flying Trunk (2)

In her bedroom, he found her sleeping. She was so beautiful he just had to kiss her. She woke up and was very frightened. But the son told her that he was the Turkish god and that he had come out of the air, and then she was glad. He told her fairy stories and by the end he loved her so much he asked her to marry him. She said yes straight away. She invited him to tea the next day, and asked him to bring a fairy story as a present for her parents. As he was going, she gave him a gold-studded sword.

Now the son flew away and with the gold pieces he bought a new nightgown and later in the wood he wrote a lovely fairytale. The next day when he went to the castle, the Sultan, his wife and the whole Court was waiting. The young man was warmly welcomed, and after he had sat down, he began.

The Flying Trunk (3)

"There was once a bunch of matches who was very proud of its heritage. It ancestor, the high pine tree, was once big old tree in the forest. Each of th matches descended from him. Now the just lay there ready to be burned. Next t them was a lighter and an old iro saucepan. These two began to tell th matches about their youth.

'Yes, when we were still on the gree branch, then we were really important We had sunshine all day when the su shone, and all the little birds had to tell u stories. We knew that we were rich because some of the trees could onl dress themselves in summer, but w were always dressed in green all yea round. Now one day the woodcutter came, and the whole family had to par Our tree-leader became a mast on a ship the branches went to other places, and now we have the ability to bring light t the poor'.'' ''For me it was completel different', said the iron pot. 'Since I wa born, I have been brightly polished a fe times, and have been cooked in, but apar from that I am locked away from th world. The only interesting thing aroun here is the shopping-basket, who ofte goes to market and tells us about th people.' 'Oh, you talk too much,' said th lighter, 'let's have a party instead.'

And so everything in the kitchen began to dance and sing, and everything was in full swing when the door opened and in came the maid. Everything became quiet. The maid took the matches and made a fire with them. How they flew up and sparkled. 'Just look!' they thought. 'just look, we are the first. What a shine what a glow!' And then they were burned.'' The son ended his story.

He heard wonderful things said about them. Then he went back to the wood. But where was his trunk? It was burned. A spark from a firework had got caught there and had burned the trunk to ashes. Sadly he sat in the wood thought about his beautiful young bride. He would never see her again because she certainly wouldn't want to marry the son of a business man.

14th April

The Flying Trunk (4)

"That was a wonderful story, now you may have our daughter!" said the Sultan's wife. The wedding day was decided on and on the evening before the whole town was lit up. There were sweet and cakes for all the children. The son himself bought rockets and all sorts of fireworks. Then he put everything in his trunk and flew with it to the middle of the town where he set off his fireworks. The Turks could hardly believe it. Then he took his trunk back into the wood and wandered among the people to find out what they thought about his fireworks.

The Princess stood the whole of the next day on the roof of the castle and waited for her bridegroom, and there she stands to this very day and waits. The young man now wanders through the land as a storyteller, but his stories are no longer as happy as the one he told the Sultan.

A Squirrel Feast

Suddenly, down ran Mr. Krabbel, followed by his wife, and then came the four little children. Look now! The person lying on the ground was now no bigger than a little tree. So, *hop, hop,* the little squirrels walked all over Peter. The children took the nuts from his hair, Mrs. Krabbel took them from his jumper, while Mr. Krabbel busied himself with his shoes. Soon there were no more nuts in sight. Then all the little squirrels climbed back into their nests.

Peter was the forester's son, and he lived with his parents right at the end of the village. Peter loved to walk through the forest and play with the animals, who trusted him completely. His favourites were the Krabbels, the squirrel family, who ran up and down the trees like a reddy-brown streak of lightning.

Father Krabbel, the most elegant and the bravest squirrel in the forest, had noticed Peter one day from his high cave in the tree. Peter never went without nuts or kernels, and he said to the squirrel. "Just look, if you come down here this is what you'll get."

Mr. Krabbel cleaned himself behind the ears and decided to accept the adventure, for in Peter's hand was a big hazelnut. He raced down the branch and landed on Peter's hand, grabbed the nut and dashed as fast as lightning back up the tree. Peter then lay down on the grass and waited. He had put hazelnuts in his pullover, his shoes and in his hair.

A real conference must have been going on above, for there appeared the heads of Mr. Krabbel, his wife and the four little Krabbels. But Peter was patient.

Bernard's Garden

Bernard has been given the flower-bed under the lilac bush by his parents. "I'm

going to plant radishes," says Bernard, and soon there are many seeds lying in the moist earth. Every hour he runs there to see if anything is moving. Yes! Something is moving. And now a worm pokes out its head. "Go away!" complains Bernard, "this is my garden." And he picks up the worm and throws it far away. "What are you doing?" asks his mother. "There was a worm in my garden. It's my garden and I won't have worms there." "But the worm lives there," says mummy. "Not anymore," says Bernard triumphantly. "But a worm belongs to the earth like the sun and the air. He makes the earth so much better." So Bernard put the worm back, "But you'd better work hard," says Bernard.

17th April

Boldi and his Friends (1)

It happened on a beautiful day in late summer. Mummy hedgehog was just coming back from a walk, when she saw something before her front door that certainly didn't belong to her. A little

angry, she ran up to the thing to get rid of it, but what she saw there made a smile spread all over her face. In a tiny basket,

deep in soft covers and bound up with a green ribbon, sat a little creature with a mop of red hair, who was looking helplessly at her. Mother hedgehog decided to bring the little creature up with her own children. Father hedgehog agreed and said, "Well, we can't just let him starve." The little hedgehog children were delighted with this unexpected creature and kept asking him who he was and where he had come from. "My name is Boldi, but where I come from I don't know. Are you angry with me because of that?" And he nearly cried. But no one was angry, and he was sweet that they decided to keep him.

18th April

Boldi and his Friends (2)

A long winter came and everything lay deep in snow. But then along came spring again, all the flowers opened and all the birds began to sing.
The hedgehog family were also happier again, and Boldi had settled in well and played with the hedgehogs all day. But best of all he liked to play with his friend the frog on the meadow, who was called

Quackpeter. He told him wonderful stories about the humans, and soon Boldi wanted to go among the humans too. He ran back to the hedgehog family and told them what he wanted to do. At first they forbade it, but then they decided to ask the owl, who was very wise.

Late at night they went to the owl. The owl listened to the story and then he said: "Boldi is no hedgehog, and if he wants to go to the humans, then there is nothing you can do to stop him. On the other hand, Mrs Hedgehog brought him up, and so he should promise to come back and tell us about the humans. I can teach him the way to town." Boldi was so excited that he fell out of bed that night. The next day there was a big leaving party for the young hero. All the animals brought him presents, and even the owl came out during the daytime to see him off. The farewell was very painful for Boldi, but he said, "Goodbye for now. One day I will come back and will have many tales to tell you!" He packed up all his presents and set off through the wood to the town where the humans lived.

19th April

Boldi and his Friends (3)

Boldi went through meadows and fields until he came to the first houses. All that now lay between him and them was a river. It had rained, and a beautiful rainbow stretched over the river. Boldi thought it was a bridge and as he tried to climb on, he fell with a splash into the water. He scrambled over to the other side, where he sat down and cried bitterly.

Then along came a dog and sniffed him. Behind him came his master who looked at him astonished. He picked him up and put him in his pocket. Boldi didn't like it there at all, because it was dark and musty. He was bounced up and down because the man was obviously in a hurry. Suddenly it was still. The man had got into a tram. Boldi curiously looked out, and beside him he saw a nice shopping-basket. He quickly climbed out of the man's pocket and crept unseen into the basket. The woman got off and took him into a toy-shop, because she was a sales assistant there. Boldi crawled out of the basket and hid himself behind a teddy bear on one of the shelves. He soon found out that the toys were not alive. That was exciting! People came, chose a toy, took it to the counter where it was wrapped up and taken away.

Then in came a woman who thought Boldi was lovely. Boldi decided to let himself be sold. The woman wanted to take Boldi straight away, so the lady sold him for £1.50. Boldi was packed in a pretty box, taken away and given to little Tom for his birthday. When he saw Boldi, he exclaimed, "That's the best present I've ever had." Tom didn't want to go to bed, but then his mother let him take Boldi to bed with him. Boldi really loved Tom, and when they were alone, he told him that he was alive. Now the pair had a big secret and, happy together, they fell asleep.

20th April

Prince Peter from Porcelaine (1)

Porcelaine was a very pretty little town, and was made out of the finest porcelain. Even the king and all the inhabitants were made of the finest porcelain. Even the king and all the inhabitants were made of porcelain, even though they behaved like everybody else. Now in the town was a beautiful porcelain church, and in the tower of this church was a heavy porcelain bell. It was rung whenever

there was a festival, or when there was any danger. Unfortunately the church had one fault, it was overrun with mice. And so the King only allowed one animal into the town, a jet-black cat with yellow eyes and a funny red hat. Peter, as the cat was called, was a very good mouse-catcher. One evening Peter was creeping through the wood. Under a tree he saw three robbers. They were talking together, and when Peter heard what they were saying, he nearly died of shock.

"Hey, wouldn't it be fun to go into Porcelaine and smash everything to pieces! They would shout for help and no one would hear." Peter ran back to the town, jumped on a wall and miaowed as loudly as he could to wake up the sleeping inhabitants, but it was in vain.

Prince Peter from Porcelaine (2)

Peter rushed to the church, for he had remembered the bell. He zoomed up the tower steps, but no matter how he pulled the rope, the bell only made a low *bim* sound and then was silent again. Peter began to cry bitterly, for he could already see the robbers climbing the city wall.

The mice heard Peter's sobs, and one by one they slowly crept out of their holes. But when they saw the crying cat, they all wanted to run back to their holes. But they didn't want to be cowards, so they stayed where they were. The cat wiped the tears from his eyes and could hardly believe his eyes. So many mice in one place.

Peter must have looked worried, for the mice took courage and asked him what was wrong. Then Peter told them of the danger which was in store for Porcelaine. Then he started to cry again. "Everything is lost, everything." I can't get the bell to ring, it's too heavy for me."

"Don't worry," comforted the oldest mouse. "If everyone helps, we'll soon get the bell to work." Then he called: "Let's go, comrades, grab the rope!" And the mice and the cat pulled with all their might on the rope. Gradually the bell began to sway, and soon it was booming out all over the town. Before long all the lights were on and all the people were streaming out of their houses to see what danger was threatening them. But they didn't see the robbers, for after the first toll of the bell they had all fallen from the wall in fright, and had run away as fast as their legs could carry them.

When the King heard of Peter's brave deed he summoned him to the Palace, took off his hat and put a crown in its place. But that the church mice had helped him remained a secret.

Crystalpuss has Toothache

What a beautiful morning! Pixie Crystalpuss is sitting in his pixie house,

as the dear sun comes streaming in through the window. "Good morning, you sleepyhead, time to get up," she calls, but the little pixie would rather hide himself among the covers. *"Ouch, ouch, my tooth is killing me!"* he groans. This was exactly the tooth that the pixie dentist, Mr. Painless wanted to pull out a long time ago. "If only I'd gone at the right time!" he wailed. He got up and washed himself, and went and sat on the

bench outside his house, always with his hand over the place where his tooth was. "What's wrong?" asked the bluebells. "Usually you're so happy and singing." "I've got nothing to sing about today," says the Pixie. "I've got such terrible toothache. If only I wasn't afraid of the dentist!" But he plucked up courage, and set off to the dentist. Good old Doctor Painless has earned his name well. Soon the tooth has been pulled and all the pain went with it, and so has Crystalpuss's fear of the dentist.

Meggie has a Birthday (1)

Today is Meggie's birthday and she has made herself look especially smart. Her parents go into town to buy her a present "We've invited Mork Putz and Peggy for the afternoon."

Now Meggie is alone in the house and she soon gets terribly bored, and so she jumps onto the garden wall to see if she can find Snip from next door. There he is, and he suggests that they go visit his Aunty Munny. Meggie agrees. When they arrive, they find her writing a letter, but what a mess! The paper, the desk, the floor and even her clothes are covered in ink spots. But she doesn't care, she thinks her letter is wonderful.

Then all three go for a walk down to the fishpond. In the middle of the pond they find a mouse sitting on a stone. Munny

wants to catch the mouse, so she reaches out too far with her snout and – SPLASH! – she has fallen in. The other two try to help her and they fall in too.

Meggie has a Birthday (2)

All the cats make a big row in the pond. Treff the poodle, who is nearby, hears and comes to the rescue. He takes them

one by one by the neck and brings them to the bank. They thank him from the bottom of their hearts, but the poodle just walks modestly away. To dry their clothes they have a race, and they all run home like the wind.

The Brave Little Tailor (1)

Meanwhile, mother has already laid the birthday table. Before long the guests start to arrive. Happily the three friends manage to arrive in time for the party. Meggie thanks everyone for the presents. After the party, the cats play around on the meadow with a ball. Then, full of food and tired, they all go to bed.

One summer morning a little tailor sat at the window in his room and sewed. Then along came a farmer's wife selling plums. The tailor opened his window and shouted out "Here, I'll have some!" The woman had to climb up the steps with her heavy basket. She spread all her wares out before him, but the tailor only chose a few plums. The woman gave him what he wanted, but she was annoyed, because she had hoped for a good sale. The tailor made himself a lovely plum pie, ready to eat after he had finished his work. But then along came the flies and sat on it. He tried to chase them away, but in vain. In the end he struck at them ruthlessly. When he counted, he had killed no less that seven flies. "What a brave man I am," thought the tailor. "The whole world is going to know about this." So he made himself a belt, and wrote on it with big letters, "SEVEN IN ONE GO". The only food he could find in the house was a piece of old cheese. In front of the door he saw a bird who had got caught in the railings, and after he had set it free, he took his cheese and went out into the world.

The Brave Little Tailor (2)

The tailor had not got very far, before he came upon a giant sitting in the grass. The tailor said to him, "I'm going out into the world to seek my fortune. Do you want to come with me?" The giant laughed mockingly, but then the tailor showed him his belt. The giant was amazed, but wanted to test the little man. He took a stone in his hand and crushed it the water came running out. "Now you try it," he said. The tailor took the cheese out of his pocket and squeezed it until the juice ran out. "Somewhat better, I think," said the tailor smiling. The giant could hardly believe it, and he said to him:

"Well, let's see if you're any good at carrying things." He led the tailor to a mighty oak tree that had fallen on the ground. "If you're so strong, help me carry this tree out of the forest." The giant put the tree on his shoulders, but the tailor hid himself among the branches. Because the giant could not turn round, he would never know. After the giant had carried the tree a way, he couldn't go on any longer. As he put the tree down, the tailor sprang from his branch and grabbed the tree as though he had been carrying it the whole way. "Such a big man and you cannot carry this tree!" mocked the tailor. But the giant really couldn't go on anymore, and so he invited the tailor to spend the night with him. When they came to the cave, they found other giants sitting round the fire. The giant showed him to a bed, but it was too big, so the tailor slept in a corner. During the night along came the giant, who wanted to kill him. With a big iron bar he smashed the bed in two, and thought that he had got rid of the cheeky grasshopper.

The next morning the giants went into the forest and forgot all about the tailor. Then, suddenly, he appeared before them, and they ran off terrified, because they thought he was going to kill them all. But the tailor just wandered on to the next town where the King lived.

The Brave Little Tailor (3)

When he came to the palace he lay down on the grass and went to sleep. As he lay there, the people saw him, and read on his belt, "SEVEN IN ONE GO". They said to each other, "What is this great war hero doing here in peace times? He must be a powerful man." The people went and reported it to the King, saying that this would be a useful man if ever war broke out. And so he went into the King's service and he was given a special apartment. But the soldiers wished the tailor a thousand miles away. "What happens if we have a quarrel with him?

He will kill seven with one blow." So they all went to the King and asked for the tailor to be dismissed. The King was very sad but he didn't dare refuse. So he sent word to the tailor, saying that he had a task for him. In a wood in his Kingdom prowled two giants, who had committed many robberies, murders and burnings. No one could go near them without their lives being in danger. If the tailor killed these two giants he could have the King's only daughter as his bride. The tailor agreed at once, and the King gave him a hundred soldiers to accompany him.

When they came to the edge of the forest, the tailor said to the soldiers: "Wait here. I want to get the giants myself." He went into the forest and found the giants snoring under a tree. He filled his pockets with stones, and climbed to the top of the tree above the sleepers. Then he began throwing stones at them, and each thought the other was hitting him. Soon they began to fight, and after tearing up trees and making holes in the ground, they both fell dead on the ground. The tailor went back to the soliders and said, "The work is done!" But the soldiers didn't believe him and went into the forest, where they found the two dead giants. Then the little tailor demanded the reward the King had promised him.

79

The Brave Little Tailor (4)

The King, however, broke his word, and would not let the tailor marry his daughter. He wanted to get rid of him. He said to him: "You must perform another heroic deed. There is a unicorn running around in the wood who is doing a lot of damage. You must catch him." So the tailor went into the wood and took with

him a rope and an axe. Soon the unicorn came towards him and began to charge at him. The tailor ran towards a tree and then quickly darted behind it. The unicorn, however, couldn't stop running, and crashed into the tree with its horn, and there he was . . . stuck! Then the tailor put the rope around his neck, hacked the horn from the tree with his axe, and led the unicorn to the King. But the King still would not part with his daughter. He had another task for the tailor. He wanted him to catch a wild boar that was also causing a lot of damage in the forest. "Gladly!" said the tailor, "This is child's play!"
Again he went into the forest, and soon along came the boar. The boar charged at him with bared teeth and a slobbering mouth. The tailor ran away from him into an old chapel and jumped straight out

through the window. The boar sprang in after him, and the tailor went back to the door and locked it. There the boar was . . . trapped! Now the King had to keep his promise, and the tailor married the Princess and got half the Kingdom. When the King died, the tailor reigned as King for the rest of his life.

Mia the Piggy-box (1)

Somehwere in a big workshop, piggy-banks were made. On each pig's back is a slit where you put your money in. But one of the pigs was given a crooked lid with a crooked split. The shopkeeper didn't know what to do with it. But one day along came a lady who bought it for her godson. Her godson had had other piggy banks which had mysteriously fallen from their shelves whenever Kevin

wanted something special. This time Kevin's aunty asked him to try and keep the pig until it was completely full. Kevin promised. Soon afterwards, however, the fair came to town and Kevin had soon spent the money his father had given him to spend. Now he tried to open Mia, for this is what he had christened the pig. But it was in vain. Then he threw it with all his might onto the floor, but the little pig was determined to keep all the money in his stomach. Kevin wanted to buy a magnifying glass, and again he tried to break the pig, but he couldn't. As it happened, Kevin's father bought him a magnifying glass. How glad Kevin was that he still had his money and the glass as well. It was quite nice to feel the pig getting heavier and heavier. He began to work harder to get even more money to feed the pig with, and when Kevin's father saw how hard he was trying, he also gave Kevin money from time to time to help him.

Mia the Piggy-box (2)

One day the boys were playing in the park. On a bank sat an old man with his dog, who was happily rolling around on the grass with the boys. But the old man was crying. The boys asked him what was wrong: "Tomorrow I've got to get rid of my dog because I can't afford to pay for the licence." The children thought that was terrible, but how could they help the old man? Then Kevin remembered his piggy box, which was already very heavy. He ran home like lightning and told his mother about the old man and his dog. His mother told him to go and fetch them both, so Kevin ran back, hoping that they were still there. While they were eating coffee and cakes – the dog was given milk – the old man told them about himself. Kevin's mother then fetched the piggy box and opened it with some tweezers. There was enough inside to pay for the dog licence, and Kevin was allowed to give it to the man. The man thanked him with tears of joy in his eyes,

1st May

The Dear Little Sunny Ray

Buzz, buzz, little bee, come from your hive,
Hello, friendly hedgehog, May's alive!
Little Tina's left some milk,
Upon the grass with its new green silk.
But now the clock is striking eight,
I'd better go, or I'll be late.

2nd May

The Pixie School

It's not only you who has to go to school — Pixies do too. Pim and Persil would love to stay in bed a little while longer, but it's a long way to school and it's time to get up! So they quickly splash cold water on their faces and sit at the breakfast table, while mother makes sure they haven't forgotten anything. They start off to school, but forget about the time and start playing in the meadow. Of course they are late for school. Their teacher is angry with them and says, "What would it be like if everyone came to school whenever they wanted!" They are very sorry, and decide to work very hard that day. They volunteer to say everything they know about the squirrel and later when they read, they do better than ever before. Then school's over and they get their coats and caps and run home. When

they get home they tell their parents everything, how they played in the meadow and were late for school. After they have admitted everything they feel much better, and soon from the pixie house comes the delicious smell of cooking.

82

The Old Oak Tree

she decides to move in there. Crying, the dwarfs leave their homes where they have been happy for so long. The oak tree is very sad, but it gets worse! Soon all the

On the edge of a big wood stands a thick oak tree. She has stood there many hundreds of years and looks happily out into the country, for her trunk is divided up into little flats, in which live a happy little community. Down below among the roots live the dwarfs. In the twilight they come out and make music. The birds, who live in the branches, sing all day, and deers and rabbits hop by to listen in.

But one day peace no longer rules in the wood. The wild cat is prowling through the wood, and all the animals and plants hold their breath when she passes by. The wild cat is hungry. All the animals in the wood daren't come out of their homes, so she has been forced to seek her prey elsewhere. When she sees the oak tree with its decorated apartments,

other animals leave their homes, for the cat is hungry and they fear for their lives.

The Old Oak Tree (2)

The poor old oak tree tries to think of a way to get rid of this unwelcome guest, but it can't think of anything.

Alone and deserted, the tree is left behind, with only the angry cat prowling through her roots and branches, looking for the eggs the birds have left behind. The old oak tree starts to cry and cry, until a lake forms among its roots, and because it can't stop crying, the lake soon floods the lower homes. The wild cat hates water and she can't swim either.

She just manages to save herself from drowning, and after she has escaped from the tree, she runs off, terrified, to another wood, and is never seen again. But the lake of tears has overflown, and flows right down the mountain. There it comes to rest in a dried-up pond, where two sad frogs live. They wonder over the fresh water, and follow the stream up until they reach the old oak tree.

The oak tree tells them of her misery. "We'll fetch your friends back for you!" exclaim the frogs, and they hop off in search of the dwarfs. After long searching, they find the dwarfs in their new homes and tell them what has happened to the oak tree. Overjoyed they pack up their little bundles again and wander back to their wood, accompanied by all the animals. The old oak tree cries a few more tears of joy when she sees her old friends come back, but then the stream stops flowing. The dwarfs set about cleaning out the tree, and while all the furniture is drying in the sun, they decide to have a party. The whole wood comes back to life, and while the party is going on, the birds come back and build new nests in the branches. When the moon is high in the sky, all the dwarfs and animals are asleep in their old beds again, never again to be threatened by a wild cat.

True Friends

Ellen, the Circusmaster's daughter, was just four years old when Konrad the lion was born on her birthday. "That's your birthday present," said her father. "Other little girls get a doll, you get a lion." So the two grew up together, played together, and loved each other very much. They both grew up, but their friendship was still as strong as ever. No one could handle Konrad anything like as well as Ellen. Today they are to do their first big number. The white mate is still a bit afraid of her dangerous rider, for Konrad has to ride on her back and jump through a hoop. But Snowflake needn't worry when Ellen is there, just a glance or friendly word, and Konrad is as obedient as a dog. The lion even eats from her hand, and after the successful performance, she fills his plate with honey which he quickly gulps down.

6th May

The Weathercock (1)

Once upon a time on a church tower, there lived a weather-cock. He had looked down from there for many years onto the world, but now he was tired of it and wanted to see what the world was like down below. So one night when all was still, he climbed down and hid until dawn. Then he went to the hen yard, stood on the manure heap and called: "I am the weather cock, and I'm going to stay here a while." "Oho!" called back the Yard Cock. "That's out of the question, you queer bird! I'm master here, and I'm telling you to go." So the poor weather cock ran away without a word, while the other hens cackled behind him. The weather cock was upset, he hadn't expected that and, quite out of breath, he hid himself again. "I'll show that proud cock!" But he closed his eyes and slept until midnight, when someone called his name and woke him up. What he saw in the bright moonlight was so strange that his heart missed a beat. It was the scarecrow. The scarecrow said, "My dear weather cock, I can see you're upset by the paleness of your beak. Listen! Once a pixie taught me magic.

With 1, 2, 3, I can give you what you want!" And before the weather cock knew what was happening, he had a red collar and feathers just like normal hens. Overjoyed he began to crow, and the moon said, "*Shhh!* You'll wake up all the animals". Soon, hedgehogs, mice and deer gathered round and wondered over this mad cock. But he didn't care, he went straight off to the farm.

"What liars these cocks are," said the fox, and made off with his prey. But when he took a bite and stumped his teeth against tin instead of meat, he was so angry he tore off all the cock's new feathers, and ran off to the hen yard to find something better. The next day, Monika the hen found the weather cock and, feeling sorry for him, she took him back to the hen yard. The cock was there too, and he apologised for what he had done. So you see the story had a happy ending. The weather cock was happy to go back to his tower, and he swears he will never travel again. It is lovely up here after all!

7th May

The Weather Cock (2)

"Now I'll show that proud cock and his hens," he thought, but he didn't see the fox. "You've come just in time," he growled, and took the cock by the neck, slobbering at the mouth. "Please put me down," screamed the cock, "I'm sure I won't taste very nice, I'm made of tin."

Clicker the Robber

The night is still and dark. Suddenly a window pane smashes. The robber Clicker climbs into Randall's toyshop, and shines a torch around. Then he steals a few things, climbs out again and disappears. The next morning Mrs. Randall comes and wonders why the building bricks are lying on the floor; they belong in the blue bag – but it's gone! She calls her husband. He notices the hat stand has fallen down and his green hat and red umbrella have gone. When Mrs. Randall comes to the toy shelves, she realises they have been robbed. "Help! Thief!" she calls.

The thief stole the green hat, red umbrella, a teddy bear, a wooden train and a ball. I wonder if the thief is playing with the ball!

The Tailor's Three Sons (1)

Once upon a time there was a tailor, who had three sons and a goat. Because the goat nourished the family with her milk, she needed good food, and every day the sons took it in turns to take her out on the meadow. One day it was the eldest son's turn. He took her to the churchyard where he let her eat as much as she could. Then he asked her, "Have you had enough?" and the goat replied, "I'm so full I couldn't eat another leaf!"

Later the tailor asked his son if the goat had had enough to eat and the son said, "She's so full she couldn't eat another leaf!" But the tailor wanted to make sure, so he went to the goat and asked her if she was full. The goat said, "How can I be full? All I did was jump over gravestones and I couldn't find a single leaf!" The tailor went back to his son and said angrily, "You liar! You would let the goat starve!" And he took a stick and chased his son out of the house.

The next day the second son took the goat out to the garden hedge. Where the goat ate everything in sight. When he asked the goat if she'd had enough, the goat said, "I'm so full I couldn't eat another leaf!" Again the tailor asked his son if the goat had had enough, and he said yes. But when the tailor asked the goat, he got the same answer as before, and the second son was chased out of the house. The next day the third son took the goat out. But by the end of the day *he* was also being chased out of the house by his father.

Now all his sons were gone, the tailor had to take the goat out himself. He let the goat eat all day, asked if she had had enough, and took her home, but when he asked her in her stall whether she was full, she gave him the same answer as when his sons had taken her out. Then the tailor realised she had been lying, and he angrily chased her out with a whip. Sadly he thought of his sons, but no one knew where they were.

10th May

The Tailors Three Sons (2)

The eldest son had gone into apprenticeship with a carpenter. He worked very hard, and when his time was up he wanted to travel. His master gave him a little table, which was made of ordinary wood, but when he said to it, "Table, Lay yourself!" it covered itself with the most wonderful food. The young man was pleased, because it would't matter now if an inn was good or bad, he would always have good food. Then he decided to go home, for surely his father would not be angry anymore. On the way home he came to an inn, and everyone made him welcome, but told him they couldn't feed him very well. The man laughed, put down his table, said, "Table, lay yourself!" and immediately it was full of food. The young man invited everyone to eat with him, so everyone tucked in.

The innkeeper watched all this, and decided to steal the table, so in his loft he found a table that looked exactly like the magic one, and swapped them over while the carpenter was asleep. The next morning, he paid and set off home. He arrived at midday. His father was overjoyed to see him. The carpenter told his father about his magic table and told him to invite all their friends and relations round for supper. When the company was gathered, he called, "Table! Lay yourself!" But nothing happened. There he stood, looking like a liar, while everyone laughed at him. He was so ashamed he went away and took up work with another master.

11th May

The Tailor's Three Sons (3)

The second son had gone into apprenticeship with a miller. When his time was over, the miller said to him, "Because you have worked so hard, I am going to give you this donkey. When you stand him on a cloth and say "Bricklebrit!" he spits out golden coins." The second son also decided to go back home, thinking that his father would surely forgive him when he saw the donkey. On the way home, he stopped at the same inn as his brother. The innkeeper wanted to put the donkey in the stall, but the miller insisted on doing it himself. After he had eaten and wanted to pay, he found he did not have enough money in his purse, so he told the innkeeper he would come straight back, and he went to the stall with a cloth in his hand. The innkeeper was very curious and followed him. The miller went into the stall and locked the door, but the innkeeper watched him through a hole in the door. His eyes nearly popped out when he saw what the donkey did, and when the miller was sleeping he exchanged the magic donkey for another one.

The next day the miller set off with his donkey, and reached his home by midday. Again all friends and relations were invited to watch the donkey perform, but it soon became obvious that the donkey couldn't do the trick. The miller realised he had been tricked, and apologised as he sent everyone home as poor as they had come. Sadly, the second son had to find himself a new master too.

The Tailor's Three Sons (4)

The third brother had gone into apprenticeship with a turner. Because it is a very skillful trade, he took longer to learn. His brothers had written to him and told him their misfortunes. When his time was up, his master gave him a cudgel. "When someone has done something against you, just call out, "Cudgel, out of your sack!" and it beats the person so hard that they can't sit down for a week. It won't stop until you tell it to go back in its sack." The turner thanked him, and set off home, and on the way, he also passed by the same inn where his brothers had been cheated. He went in and bégan to say, "Yes, it's easy to find a table that lays itself, and a donkey that spits out coins, but that's nothing compared to the treasure I've got!" The innkeeper pricked up his ears, and thought the sack must contain precious stones. "I've got to have them." he thought. When the innkeeper thought the young man was asleep, he crept into the room with another sack, in order to change it with the other. But the turner was waiting for him. He called, "Cudgel, out of your sack!" and the cudgel set about the innkeeper. The louder the innkeeper cried, the harder the cudgel beat him. "If you want me to call the cudgel off," said the turner, "give me the magic table and the donkey!" The innkeeper rushed and got them straight away, and the turner called off the cudgel and set off home to his father.

The Tailor's Three Sons (5)

The tailor was overjoyed when he saw his youngest son. The son told him about his trade, his gift and that he had also redeemed the other gifts of his brothers. Again the friends and relatives were called, but they came only with great persuasion. But this time the miller spread a cloth on the floor, put the donkey on it, called "Bricklebit!" and the donkey spat out so much gold that the people could hardly carry it! The carpenter was given the table, he called,

"Table, lay yourself!" and the table became full of the best food. What a feast they had that night! The tailor locked away his cloth and needles, and lived happily ever after with his sons. But what became of the goat no one knows!

Mother's Lullaby

Sleep, little baby, close your eyes,
While mummy sings a lullaby.
The beetle sleeps, the ladybird too,
The deers are tired, just like you.

Sleep, little baby, or you'll hear,
The owl with his hooting flying near.
He'll land by the window and in he'll peep,
To screech at you if you're not asleep.

Sleep, little baby, a kiss I'll take,
And then I'll watchfully stay awake.
Daddy comes soon and he'll bring a cake,
That tomorrow a fine sweet bite will make.

The Ladybird and the Bee

The little ladybird with the seven spots on its red wings had flown around in the sunshine all day. In the afternoon it was in my garden, and chased away the nasty little bugs from my roses.

"Buzzzzzz," heard the ladybird, and along came a bee. "Have you come because of the bugs too?" she said.

"What do I want with bugs?" said the bee, "I've come to fetch the honey from the roses, and put it in the pocket in my leg. Then I'm going to my beehive."

"How lovely," sighed the ladybird. "Who do you live with in the beehive?"

"With my Queen and many other bees," said the bee. Then he filled his pockets and flew to the next flower, leaving the ladybird a little sad. Suddenly it noticed it was getting dark, and it was time to find a place for the night.

But then the ladybird saw a light that was nearly as bright as the sun, and so she flew towards it. And do you know where she landed? She flew right through my window. Otherwise she wouldn't have been able to tell me this story.

Puppet Burli and the Cat Murli (1)

There was once a little girl who had a puppet called Burli. When one day the little girl got a kitten, the cat and the puppet became best friends. After a while, the kitten got homesick for the island on which it was born. The puppet thought for a while and then said: "In the toybox is a sailing ship in which we can sail over the lake!" He lifted the ship onto a car which he pulled himself, and Murli the cat got in too. When they got to the lake, they put the ship in the water and climed in. The wind blew the sails and the ship began to move. But the wind became stronger and Murli was afraid, but Burli said, "Don't be afraid! Look, I'm not afraid at all!"

That made the wind angry, and he blew so hard that the waves started going into the boat. "Please, dear wind, be good to us!" begged Burli, and the wind softened and led the ship further until it came to the island.

Puppet Burli and the Cat Murli (2)

Burli and Murli climbed onto the bank, and saw a little town with houses that had roofs like onions. In the town lived

cats and pixies. The cats were all dressed like people, but they all had very serious faces. The puppet tried to make them laugh, but they refused even to smile. Then one of the pixies explained, "Our King has forgotten how to laugh, therefore it is forbidden for us to laugh either!"

"Take me to the King!" said the puppet, and the pixie took the puppet and the cat to the King's palace. On a golden throne sat the King of the Island, with a long white beard, and a very serious face. The puppet tried his best tricks on the King, but nothing worked, Burli was so sad that in the end he had a long face too.

But that looked so funny that the King almost split his sides laughing! Then the King summoned his photographer and had his picture taken with Burli and Murli, and then had the photo displayed outside the Palace walls. How happy everyone was that the King could laugh again!

too quickly. Peter can have great fun with the cockchafers. They climb along a strung-out piece of wool, but you have to be careful when they start to 'pump', because then they're getting ready to fly away. A few have flown away already, and before long the whole box is empty.

Then Burli and Murli visited the little cat's parents and brothers and sisters, then rushed back down to the lake, where they found the King waiting by the ship. He had come to wish them farewell. Burli promised to come back soon and then he pushed off, while all the cats and pixies waved with brightly-coloured handkerchiefs. By evening the ship had reached the other bank. The little girl had been looking for them, and they were all happy to be together again.

Cockchafers (1)

May is here, and with it comes swarms of Cockchafers buzzing through the air. Like all children, Peter likes to shake the thick beatles from the trees, and the empty cigar box with the holes in it is full only

But Peter's sister Chrystal knows where they can find loads of cockchafers to fill the box with: behind the house in the garden. Although today she is a nurse and she's very busy because Teddy and her dolls are ill, playing with cockchafers is also good fun. Chrystal shakes so many beetles from the tree that they have to put them in a shoe box instead. Peter has never had so many, and he's very proud.

Cockchafers (2)

After the beetle gathering, both children are very hungry. Then mother calls them in for supper. They all tuck in, and nobody notices that the scrabbling inside the box is getting louder, and that the lid is being lifted up. Soon the room is crawling with cockchafers, they are creeping all over the supper table. Daddy in his fright upsets his soup, and there's one crawling in mummy's hair. Peter's eyes nearly pop out! "I didn't think they'd be able to lift the lid off!" he said, "I didn't think they'd be strong enough for that."

"One wouldn't be!" says daddy, pushing one out of his face, "But you've shut a whole army in that box!"

Mummy runs to the window and flings it open, and out flies the first beetle, happy to have its freedom back. Then Peter lets the rest fly out of the box, he doesn't want them to be unhappy. "Goodbye, Cockchafers! How nice it is for the children that you come back every year!"

The May Parade

Come with me among the trees,
You don't need money, the entrance is free.
On a stump stands the hare and calls out loud for all the creatures to join the crowd.
The squirrels, the moles, the badgers brave,
Are gathering for the May parade.

The sparrow, the blackbird, the starling gay,
Are singing a song to beautiful May.
Come with me among the trees.
You don't need money, the entrance is free.

Petal's Rollerskates

Petal has got some rollerskates for her birthday, and she wants to try them out straight away. Then along comes Susi, Petal's friend. "Come quickly! I want to show you something!" Susi's doll has just been given some new clothes, and they try them all on, one after the other. Meanwhile, however, the right skate has rolled down to Lassie's kennel. The dog sniffs it curiously, then drags it into his house. How upset Petal is when she comes back and finds her skate missing. "The police have dogs that search for things," says Susi. "Take the left shoe to Lassie, she'll find the other one." Petal rushes with the skate to Lassie and lets her sniff it. "Now find the other one!" she says. Another strange thing like the other one, thinks Lassie, so she goes into her kennel and brings out the other one to the amazed Petal.

The Princess and the Pea

There was once a Prince, who led a happy life in his parent's castle. One day his father said to him: "I am getting old and tired, and when I die, you will make a good King. But you need a Queen. Find yourself a wife!"

So the Prince decided to travel around the world and find himself a Princess, but it had to be a *real* Princess. But that was much more difficult than he had imagined. Yes, there were plenty of Princesses, but none of them seemed real, there was always something wrong somewhere, and so he came home very troubled.

One evening there was a terrible thunderstorm, and while this storm was raging around the castle, a knock came on the door, and the old King himself went to open it. Before him stood a Princess! The King hurried her inside and had a hot bath prepared for her. Everyone remarked how beautiful she was, but all she would say was, "I am a real Princess!" The Prince liked the Princess very much, and he wished with all his heart that she was a real Princess.

The Queen also wanted to make sure, and she had an idea. She fetched a pea from the kitchens and laid it under the mattress where the Princess was to sleep. Then she loaded several other mattresses on top of it, and the Princess was to sleep right at the top. The Princess was very tired from her day, and after supper she went straight to bed, but she couldn't sleep. The pea under the mattresses dug into her so hard that by morning she was black and blue. Only a real Princess could be so sensitive. How happy the Prince was! He had travelled all through the land looking for a real Princess, and now the most beautiful of all had come to him! They had a wonderful wedding, but the pea was laid on a velvet cushion and put in a glass case, where it can still be seen today.

Dudu and his Three Little Friends

There was once a little boy called Dudu, who had three little rubber friends: the white sealion Wowo, the pink bear Wuwu, and the duck Wiwi. One day his two little sisters took him for a walk. They proudly took him into the park, where he was given a bag of old bread to feed the ducks with. Without noticing, he threw his little toy duck in as well. It was found the next morning and given to the park-keeper to look after, but meanwhile Dudu and his sisters moved on to the deer meadow. Kiki, one of the little deers came right up to the fence, and Dudu was so excited that he jumped up and down in his pram, causing the little bear to fall out of his pocket. Later on it was found by a dog, who took it to his little wife, who gave it to the park-keeper.
Meanwhile as Dudu and his sisters walked on, a storm blew up, and they sheltered for a while. When it was over they set off home and on the way Dudu reached out to one of the puddles, and doing so dropped his sealion. This was later found by the park-keeper When Dudu got home, he cried bitterly because he had lost his three friends, but the next day, mummy took him back to the park and went to the park-keeper. Sure enough, on the shelf were the three rubbery friends. Dudu hugged them with a shout of joy.

oldi and the Circus (1)

There he saw a trail of gaily-coloured waggons, carrying animals like those he had once lived with in the wood. Boldi was simply delighted.

Can you remember Boldi? He was given to Tom as a birthday present, and was allowed to sleep in his bed. But look what happened! Tossing and turning in the night, Tom accidentally pushed Boldi out of bed onto the floor. Boldi woke up with a start, and he started to cry bitterly, for he thought Tom didn't love him anymore. He cried all night, and then he said to himself: "I'll leave Tom!" and at this thought he began to cry again, for he loved Tom very much.

Full of sorrow he ran through the garden, out through the fence and onto the street, where he found a big bag. It belonged to the paper-boy, who was already up delivering the morning papers. Boldi climbed into the bag, and when the boy came back, he lifted the bag up and rode off on his bike. The next time he put down his bag, Boldi jumped out and ran round the corner where he heard a loud noise.

Boldi and the Circus (2)

Boldi followed the Circus people, climbed into a waggon and hid himself. He rode with it to the Square where a huge tent had been put up. He sprang from the waggon, and suddenly found himself behind the stage. Later, the first

show began, and Boldi was amazed when he saw the things going on. Past him ran a man with a white face, carrying a live monkey on his shoulder. Then he saw a beautiful lady dancing on an elephant. Then came a black-haired girl walking on a rope! Boldi just had to have a go too! He managed to reach the rope without being seen. The children began to laugh, for they thought he belonged to

the Circus. The Orchestra didn't know what was happening and they carried on playing. Boldi did a wonderful somersault, and the audience screamed with delight. The Circus-master screamed too, but with terror! Then it happened – Boldi did a high jump, lost his balance and crashed to the ground. The people laughed, but Boldi was ashamed, it wasn't so easy to walk the tightrope!

26th May

Boldi and the Circus (3)

Boldi ran away as fast as he could, crying with disappointment. He wanted to be alone, so he climbed into a blue car that stood by the side of the road. He fell asleep, and didn't notice that the owner had come back. The owner started the car, and it wasn't until the car stopped suddenly that Boldi woke up. Then Mr. Teacher saw him. "Who are you?!" he asked, astonished. Then Boldi began to tell his story, and when he talked about Tom he bacame sad again. But when the teacher heard about Tom, he said, "Ah! I think I can help you!"

Meanwhile Tom had woken up, and felt happy because he could play with Boldi – but he had disappeared! Tom looked for him everywhere, and called out to him, but finally, in despair, he started to cry. His mother and father couldn't comfort him, and at night Tom didn't sleep a wink.

On Monday he didn't feel like going to school, but in the end he did, but he was very sad. In the classroom, someone climbed up beside him, and Tom could hardly believe his eyes! It was Boldi! The teacher had brought Boldi to school with him. Tom cried with joy, and everyone could understand why!

27th May

The Ugly Duckling (1)

It was summer. At the water's edge sat a duck hatching her eggs. One after the other the eggs cracked. *"Peep, peep!"* went the ducklings, and they were so sweet! But what came out of the last

egg?! A big, extremely ugly chick! The duck looked at it in dismay, and then waddled off to the pond with her children. The ugly duckling swam just as well as the other chicks, and because the mother duck had a good heart, she loved this chick as well. "Now we're going to the duckyard, follow me!" she said, and they all swam off. The other ducks were delighted with all her children, except for the last one, whom they didn't like at all.

The most important duck flew up to it and bit it! The mother was very upset, but she couldn't stop the cock and all the hens from mocking it. The ugly duckling got sadder and sadder, until it couldn't take any more and it ran away. It came to a big heath, where all the wild ducks live. But even the wild ducks found it ugly, and only a couple of wild geese befriended it. One day, however – "Bang, Bang," resounded through the air, and the two geese dropped dead. It was a hunt, and soon a big hound came towards the duckling. But the hound ran past it. "Thank God I'm so ugly!" thought the duckling, "Even the dog doesn't want to bite me!" When it got dark, the duckling ran out, and came to a little house where an old woman and her cat lived. It stayed there for a while, until it started to long for water again, so it left. But now it was autumn, and as the weather got colder, a hard time began for the duckling.

The Ugly Duckling (2)

One evening when there was a beautiful sunset, a flock of swans flew by. The duckling felt a strange pulling at its heart, and an inexplicable love for these birds.

Then came winter, and it was so cold! The duckling swam between the blocks of ice to stop the water from freezing, but one day it was so tired that it couldn't swim anymore, and the water froze. Early the next morning a farmer came and took pity on the duckling, and took it home with him. There it came back to life. Finally the weather got warmer and soon came the Spring. Then the duckling took to its wings for the first time and, as luck would have it, it landed in a beautiful garden. Three gorgeous swans came swimming by, and when they saw the duckling they came nearer. The duckling bowed its head with respect as they came

nearer. But what did it see there in the clear water? The ugly duckling had disappeared, and in its place was a beautiful swan. The three swans swam around their new acquaintance, and stroked it with their wings. Two children came into the garden and wondered over the beauty of this new swan. The swan was quite overcome with happiness, and hid its head in its wing. But the swan was neither proud nor vain, for it had suffered a lot. I never dreamed this would happen to me, it thought.

Clicker the Robber is Caught

Mr. Randall goes to the telephone and rings Detective Snuffel, who comes straight away. He looks around the shop, and notes down in his book everything that was stolen, then he sets off on the trail of the robber immediately. He watches everyone on the street very closely. Do you know how he can recognise the robber? Think for a while what the robber stole. He has probably put the toys in a blue . . ., on his head he is wearing a green . . ., as well as that he has the red . . . . Aha! Our detective has already found someone with a red umbrella – but he has no green hat or blue sack. It's only old Mr. Myers walking his dog. Wait a minute! Is that him? But our Detective has left his glasses at home; can you help him?

Hamie the Chequered Pony

In Green-meadow, the pony stable, there was great rejoicing. Miriam the pony had given birth to a pair of chequered ponies. Little Lisa always stayed by her mother's side in the field, but Hamie was headstrong and brave, and often ran away from them. One day he ran away to another field where the big brown and gentle Shirehorse was pulling the plough. On he ran, and by dawn he came to a mountain, from the top of which he could see a schoolyard. When the children saw him, they ran up to him and shouted, "Please, don't run away, little pony!" When they started feeding him with sugar lumps, he loved it. Then, later, he came to a big tent on a green meadow – a circus! Horses, donkeys, monkeys, camels, lions and giraffes all over the place! Now Hamie had really seen the world and wanted to go home again. He met the shepherd, who took him back home with his sheep. Hamie went to his mother, "How lovely it is to be back home!"

The Five Handkerchiefs

Five handkerchiefs went on a journey in the train. On the way they spoke to each other.

"Children will put us in their pockets."

"Will it be fun there?"

A red handkerchief said: "Yes, just wait. You'll be put in a trouser pocket where nails and wire will make holes in you. If you get a boy, he'll use you to clean his shoes or polish his pebbles."

"But we're made to blow noses," said the others.

"You wait and see! They only blow their noses on their sleeves!"

"Do girls treat you any better?"

"Oh, horrible girls! They'll use you as cleaning rags, and then they'll lose you somewhere."

One of the handkerchiefs began to cry. Then a white hanky began to speak: "I was once a serviette, and the children were very good to me. They liked to keep their hankies in good condition. Little Mary will wash you, and then she hangs you out on the line to dry in the sun, and that's great fun!" To the hanky who was crying he said: "Little David takes you in his hand and waves you out of the window when someone comes."

Now the hankies felt happier, and each hoped to get a good child. They would always meet up on the washing line, and would be able to tell each other what had happened to them.

The Dear Little Sunny Ray

"Today I'll stay," says our sunny ray,
"I want to watch the children play.
Oh, June! You've made the meadow gay,
With bluebells, roses and yellow hay.
There's little Tina crouching down,
How lovely is her flowery crown!"

My Little Sister

I love my little sister very much. She says such funny things that everyone has to laugh. She's called Babby and I'm called Irene. I'm already nine years old, a really grown-up girl. I can already go shopping on my own, water the flowers – things that Babby can't do. Babby cries when she has to go to sleep, but when she smiles at mum and dad, they forget all their anger. But they don't forget their anger when I smile at them. I think they love Babby much more than me, and that's why I'm going to granny's tomorrow, she loves me the best. Although I'm nine years old, I'm still stupid. Today I went to granny's after school without telling my mum. When it was dark outside the doorbell rang – there stood my mum with eyes red from crying. When she saw me, she put Babby on granny's knee and pulled me to her tight. "Darling! I was so worried about you!" she said. Now I know how much my mum loves me and my sister.

Elsie and wanted to be a good mother, but Elsie was very stubborn with her – she simply didn't want to become a Lady! She liked running around in an old blue dress and dirty boots. She wasn't interested in learning, she was much more interested in animals, especially now that the dog Diana had just had puppies. Every morning Elsie rushed to the breakfast table straight from the stables without washing, and with bread in one hand and marmalade in the other, she told her stories about the horses, not noticing the looks on her parents' faces. One day they told her she would be going to a girls' boarding school on the 1st of July. Elsie said nothing but ran out of the room, crying with anger.

3rd June

The Story of Elsie (1)

Elsie was a very sweet girl. She lived with her father and her stepmother, for her mother was dead. Her stepmother loved

4th June

The Story of Elsie (2)

Mrs. Macket began to get Elsie's clothes ready. Secretly, Elsie packed her blue

well educated here. Miss Gus, a young teacher, took Elsie to her room. There she was introduced to a young lady called Nellie, whose real name was Elinor Grey.

dress and blouse, and a bottle with her frog in it. The day came and, crying, Elsie said goodbye to Diana and her puppies. Her mother wanted to kiss her, but Elsie turned her back on her. Her father took her to the school, which was right up in the mountains. When the train started off, she felt more desolate than ever in her life. Soon her father would leave her, and she would be completely alone in a strange place. When they got to the school, all Elsie's stubborness disappeared, and she threw her arms around her father and sobbed. "Ah, child," he comforted, "a year will soon pass and then you'll be with us again." Elsie looked at her father, and said she would only go if she could take Bob the puppy with her!

"I'll look after her!" said Nellie.
Then Elsie had to say goodbye to her father and the puppy, for it wasn't allowed to stay. Nellie wanted to help her unpack, but Elsie just threw all her nice clothes into the drawers. At supper, Elsie took four pieces of bread, put two on top of each other and gobbled them quickly down. Then she slurped down her milk, with both elbows on the table. After the meal, Nellie had to show Elsie how she should put her serviette through the ring and not just crumple it up on the table.

The Story of Elsie (3)

The door of Miss Ray's boarding school was opened by a girl. Elsie looked around uncomfortably, but the place seemed to please her father – she would certainly be

The Story of Elsie (4)

After eating, most of the girls went for a walk in the garden, so Nellie and Elsie went too. Then it was time to go to bed. The head of the school held Elsie back for a while, and told her to have more manners at the dinner-table, and not to swallow everything down like a pig. Elsie turned a deep red with shame, ran to her bedroom and burst into tears. The next morning one of the girls said to her,

"What a noise you made last night with all that wailing!" Elsie walked out, very hurt, but Miss Gus went after her and called her back. After she had done an examination, it was decided that she should go into the second class. She spent that night unpacking properly with Nellie. Nellie thought her old clothes were terrible, but it was a very pleasant evening and Elsie knew for sure that she had made a good friend.

7th June

Furry's Adventure

One beautiful summer's day, mummy allowed Burt and his sister Bridget to go berry-picking in the wood. The dog Lumpy and Furry the teddy bear were also allowed to go. Burt loved the teddy more than anything, and Lumpy was jealous. Burt put Furry on a tree stump so that he had two hands free, and soon the children had moved quite a long way away, forgetting about the bear. Lumpy didn't say anything because now he had all the attention. Teddy got so lonely that he started to cry. A hare came by and asked him what was wrong. "Oh! Have you seen Burt and Bridget anywhere?" he wailed. "Yes," said the hare, "I'll take you to them, they're by the pond." But when they got there the children had already gone, and Teddy started to cry again. Then along came Quack the duck, and when Teddy told her what had happened, she put him on her back and carried him over the pond. Teddy was glad to be on firm ground again. Still the children were nowhere to be seen, and Teddy just laid down and cried. Burt was also crying bitterly at home, when he realised he had lost Furry. Lumpy was so

moved by Burt's tears, that he quickly ran back to find the bear, and when he found him by the pond, he carried him home. They have been the best of friends ever since.

The Wolf and the Seven Kids (1)

Then he went back to the goats' house and called out in such a sweet voice that they thought it was their mother. But one of the kids demanded: "Show us your feet first!" The wolf put one black foot under the door. "You're not our mother!" cried the goats, shocked. "Our mother has white feet. You're the wolf!" Furious, the wolf ran to the stream and dipped in his feet. Then he ran to the miller and demanded that he sprinkled flour on them. The miller didn't want to, but the wolf theatened to eat him if he didn't. With his new white feet the wolf ran back to the house for the third time. After having called out in his sweet voice and shown them his white feet, the goats opened the door. When they saw the wolf they were terrified and they all scattered to different hiding places. But he found everyone and gobbled them down. Only the youngest one hidden in the clock, was saved. After his meal, the wolf lay down under a tree in front of the house and went to sleep.

The Wolf and the Seven Kids (2)

There was once an old goat who had seven kids. One day she said to her children, "I have to go into the wood and fetch food. Beware of the wicked wolf! He's very crafty, but you can recognise him by his rough voice and his black feet." The kids promised not to let anyone into the house.

Not long afterwards there was a knock at the door, and a voice said "Open up, dear children, it's your mother!"

But the goats replied, "You're not our mother, she's got a bright voice!"

So the wolf ran to the shop and bought some chalk. He ate the chalk and soon all the roughness in his voice had gone.

When the old goat got back and saw the house in such a mess, she was very afraid. Time and again she called her children, but it was a long time afterwards when a little voice called from the clock: "I'm here, mummy!" She found her little child and kissed it joyfully, but when she heard what had happened to the others she cried enough to break her heart. Then they heard the terrible snoring of the wolf under the tree. The mother crept outside, and was about to attack the wolf. But then she saw that something was moving in his stomach.

105

"No, little duckling, there's only goose wine!"
"Then fly off alone, your taste isn't mine!"

Sly Sepp

Sepp was no beauty as a dog, but he had a heart of gold. He loved little Doris most of all, a little two year old with blonde hair. Today the little girl had played with Sepp the whole time, and now she turned to her puppet Frank. She had only had him a week, and he had already lost a leg! Doris put her fingers into the hole and pulled out handfuls of straw. Then she looked at its funny head. Suddenly she lifted up her little hands and pulled off its head! Then she held it out to Sepp and said gaily, "Puppet broken!" Sepp thought that now Doris would pull his head off and he growled at her for the first time. Really, Doris had only wanted to show that Sepp was her favourite toy.

Perhaps one of her children were still alive. She fetched scissors, needle and thread, and split the wolf's stomach right down the middle. Out jumped all six of her children, alive and well! The wolf must have swallowed them whole! How happy they all were to be back together again! But mother ordered them to fetch some heavy stones. When she had them she placed them in the wolf's stomach and sewed him up again. When the wolf woke up he felt very thirsty, so he ran to the spring, all the time wondering what was jumping around inside him. When he bent down to drink, the weight of the stones caused him to tumble into the spring, where he drowned.

Suddenly Sepp had an idea. He went over to the toy box and pulled out a stuffed dog, which he laid at Doris's feet. The stuffed dog was in perfect condition and Doris said, "Sepp not broken, Sepp nicer!" as she stroked the stuffed dog. Reassured, Sepp let Doris put her arms around him, and again they were the best of friends.

10th June

The Goose and the Duckling

"Mr. Goose, Mr. Goose, where do you go?
Tell me your secret, I do want to know!"
"I go to my friend, another old goose."
"To eat chocolate, and cakes and sweet apple juice?"

The Forest Party

In the crickle-crackle pixie house, where the birds sing and the bees hum, among the spotted toadstools and the flowers, there lives a gnome-child. Happy and gay with a blue cap on her head and a bow in each plait, she rushes around preparing for this big day. There's going to be a

Oh, it's Cola the little bear. Frank, the little mouse, has dressed up in all his finery; here is the raven with his cousin; up from the hole comes the mole, and over him hops the hare. The table is laid with all the animals' favourite food. Berries, roots, fruit salad, tarts, cakes, lemonade, puddings and honey wine. They all tuck in heartily, while more and more guests arrive at the crickle-crackle pixie house. After they have all eaten, the table is cleared. The fox sweeps the floor with his tale for the guests to dance on. The birds sing to the music of the harmonica played by the mouse, while the hare beats time with his paw. Then the dancing begins. All the guests hop, turn, clap, stamp and fly around the garden, up and down and all around, big and small. Later they are so tired after the festivities that they all curl up and go to sleep outside the crickle-crackle pixie house.

party in her garden. In the oven a big cake is baking, for every one of her friends is invited. Here come the first guests: Pim the gnome in a beautiful carriage, and who's that padding through the thicket?

107

Boldi on the Farm (1)

The holidays had come, and Tom was allowed to go to his Uncle's in the mountains. Of course he took Boldi with him. When the two friends were sitting in their train compartment, Tom went to sleep, but Boldi stared curiously out of the window. It was wonderful to see the countryside flash by, but soon he got bored with that, and he wanted more adventure. He ran out of the compartment and down the corridors. Soon he smelled a lovely smell of food, and went towards the dining-car. There a friendly man noticed him, and thinking that someone must have lost him, he picked him up and put him by his coffee cup, hoping that someone would come and find him. Not long afterwards, Tom woke up and found his little friend gone. Tom began to search everywhere, and when he finally found Boldi in the dining-car, the train drew to a halt, for they had reached the station. Boldi didn't even have time to thank the man, for they had to get out straight away.

Boldi on the Farm (2)

Uncle fetched Tom and Boldi from the station, and they travelled in a horse and cart to the farm in the mountains. While Tom was saying hello to his aunty, Boldi was making friends with the animals. Boldi told them he had been brought up in the forest, and the animals told him that the forest wasn't very far away from there. So Boldi said, "Then we'll all go there tonight! No one will notice and you can meet all my friends." That night, Boldi and the household pets slipped out into the forest, but Boldi didn't recognise the surroundings, and soon the animals got frightened. Then Boldi saw the owl. Surely he would recognise him! But when Boldi tried to introduce himself, the owl said, "Nonsense! There's never been a creature like you in this forest, it must have been another wood." Boldi cried enough to break his heart, but the Owl said, "Calm down, you'll wake the other animals. It's not so bad, you'll find your wood some day. There are many woods, just as there are many towns!" Boldi and the others were amazed, they didn't know that. Owls are very clever creatures! The other animals now tried to find the way back, and tried to comfort Boldi. They told him they weren't at all angry, they all loved him, but that now he would have to go to bed. Boldi climbed up beside Tom and cried himself to sleep.

oldi on the Farm (3)

A Bird Flies in an Aeroplane

Mrs Pipe got in a plane,
With her parrot in a cage,
The plane flew off into the air,
And the bird began to rage.

Then all at once the bird got out,
And flew round causing havoc,
So everyone got very cross
With the noisy squawking parrot!

Then a man called out as the bird flew by,
"A parrot helps a flight,
Since although you won't believe it,
It makes a plane lose weight!"

Lala and the Baby Lion (1)

he next morning as the sun shone and oldi was having breakfast on the alcony with Tom, everything seemed much better. Down in the yard, the armhands were taking out the horses nd carts to go mowing on the mountain. om wanted to go too, so with Boldi winging on a rake and laughing with lee, they both set off. Then Boldi went xploring in the field. There he met a eldmouse who was very agitated. Boldi sked her what was wrong. "Oh, they're nowing again!" she said. "It's terrible for mice, because the entrance to our holes s left wide open, and it's dangerous when there's no grass to hide it." Boldi ould well understand her problem. "But he grass will soon grow again, and then ou'll be safe," he said. That made the mouse feel better. Boldi and Tom did lots f wonderful things together, then one lay Tom's father came to fetch them in he car, for the holidays were over. Boldi vas sad, because he didn't want to part rom his friends, but on the way home he egan to laugh again, and look forward o being back.

There was once a little coloured girl called Lala. When she wasn't playing with her friend Biggy, she helped her mother in the house. One evening in the village called Kral, Lala heard a car. She ran out with the other children so as not to miss anything. A big car stopped and some white men got out. They were greeted by the village and they began to give out presents. The village prepared a big party to welcome the white men. The drums announced the party, and all the people ran over to the village square. Only Lala stayed behind, and looked into the cages that stood on and around the car. Pooh! There was a young rhinocerous shaking its head and an elephant tied to a post, who was trying to get away.

Lala and the Baby Lion (2)

A baby lion in one cage looked so sad that Lala's heart almost broke with pity. The lion came up to the bars and licked the

finger that Lala put through the bars. She wondered what she could feed the cub with, for it was certainly hungry. The cage was easy to open, and she took the cub home with her to feed it. The party was at an end, and becuase they had stayed too long they set off straight away on their journey. Meanwhile Lala had fed her friend, and now he seemed full. Then she ran with him back to the car, but it had disappeared. Suddenly she smiled, held the lion to her heart and went back to the hut. Now Lala had a friend that she could really take care of, and since the cub knew that Lala meant him no harm, he trusted her. The next morning, Lala told her friend Biggy what had happened, and Biggy thought it was wonderful, but between you and me, she was a little envious, even though she was allowed to take the medicine man's crocodile for walks! After that you could see the two children taking their animals for walks and all the other animals would shout "Look! Here comes Lala with her lion cub and Biggy with her crocodile!"

19th June

When the Sun so Brightly Smiles

When the sun so brightly smiles,
Peter gets the cart,
And off we ride into the fields,
With sunshine in our hearts.
There sits Erica with her doll,
Wearing Sunday best,
And Peep the sheepdog in the back,
Has a welcome rest.
Run, horse!

When the sun so brightly smiles,
So smiles the whole world too,
The heather waves in the sunny breeze,
And sends its scent to you.
Little mice sunbathe by their holes,
For inside it's far too hot,
They flick their whiskers dozily,
As we pick forget-me-nots.

When the sun goes slowly down,
We all ride sleepily home,
To feed the horse and tuck him in,
And leave the fields alone.
But they are waiting patiently,
For another sunny day,
While Erica, Peter, you and me,
Are far in dreams away.
It was lovely today!

20th June

The Rhubarb Leaf

You think it's impossible to tell a story
about a rhubarb leaf? Oh no, it's not! Just
listen and then tell me whether it's a story
or not! So: there was once a very sad
rhubarb leaf. Rhubarb leafs aren't very
useful, for people only ever eat the stalks.
When it was summer, the rhubarb leaf
got so sad that it got droopy. Perhaps it
also missed the rain. But one day dark

clouds covered the sky. A bee came and
settled underneath the leaf, for he had
just been gathering honey and was glad
of the shelter. Then a butterfly with
beautiful bright wings came along and
also took shelter. One drop of rain can
break a butterfly's wing. When the first
drop of rain fell, a little kitten came and
sat under the leaf, and there they waited
until the storm was over. Strengthened
by the rain, the rhubarb leaf lifted itself up
high. After all, hadn't he rescued three
helpless animals? Now, was that a story
or wasn't it?

21st June

Hansel and Gretel (1)

There was once a woodcutter, who lived
with his wife and two children on the
edge of the forest. The boy was called

"We're going to look for wood, and th[en] we'll come and fetch you." The childr[en] were tired from their walk and went [to] sleep. When they woke up it was dark a[nd] they were alone.

But as soon as the moon rose, t[he] pebbles Hans had laid shone bright[ly] and the children easily found their w[ay] home. In spite of everything, th[e] parents were overjoyed to see them.

22nd June

Hansel and Gretel (2)

But not long afterwards, their paren[ts] found themselves in great poverty on[ce] again. Again they decided to leave t[he] children in the forest, and again t[he] children heard their plan. But this time the windows were locked so that Ha[ns] couldn't fetch any pebbles. This time [as] they set off in the wood, Hans crumbl[ed] his piece of bread along the way, hopi[ng] they would be able to follow the tr[ail] home. But that night when they woke a[nd] found themselves alone, they went [to] follow the trail, only to find that the bir[ds] had eaten the bread. The children ra[n] deeper and deeper into the wood un[til] they came to a little house in a clearin[g]. The children could hardly believe it! T[he] roof was made of biscuits and cand[y] while the windows were made of sug[ar]. Hans broke a piece from the roof, whi[le] Gretel took a piece of the window. The[re] came a voice from the house:
"Crumble Crumble Craus!
Who's nibbling at my house!"
Suddenly the door opened and a[n] ancient woman came out. Hansel an[d] Gretel were terrified, but the old woma[n] said, "I'm not going to kill you, you mu[st] be very hungry. Come inside, I've g[ot] some lovely things to eat!" Because th[e] woman spoke so nicely to them, the[y] went in. Poor Hansel and Gretel! No[w]

Hansel and the girl Gretel. Although the woodcutter worked very hard, they were very poor, and one night the woodcutter's wife said. "We can't go on like this. Tomorrow we must take the children out into the forest. When they get tired and fall asleep, we must leave them there. Hopefully someone will find them that can give them more than us." But because the children were too hungry to sleep, lying upstairs in bed, they had heard what their parents said. Gretel cried bitterly, but Hans crept out and filled his pockets with pebbles, and when they were walking in the forest with their parents the next day, Hans always stayed a little way behind and made a trail with the stones. Their parents led them deep into the wood where they had never been before. Then they said:

they were in the house of a witch and they didn't know! The old woman brought out a fine cake, and soon, full up and tired, they fell among the snow white covers of their beds and thought they were in Heaven.

Hansel and Gretel (3)

But the old witch had it in her mind to fatten the children up and then eat them. The next morning she locked Hans in a narrow cage where he could hardly move, so that he would get fat quicker. Gretel had to work from morning till night. Every morning the witch would make Hans stick out his finger to see if he was fat enough to slaughter. But Hans always stuck out his knuckle, and because the witch had bad eyes, she didn't notice, but only wondered why he didn't get fat. In the end she got impatient and sent Gretel off to fetch some water. "Whether he be fat or thin, today I'm going to slaughter him and cook him!" Gretel stuttered and stammered, but in the end she had to do as she was told. Then the witch said, "Now we're going to do some baking. Creep into the oven to see if it's at the right heat." When Gretel was in the oven, the witch was going to shut the door and bake her. But Gretel knew what the witch had in mind, and she said to her, "I don't know how to do it, please show me first!" "Stupid child!" grumbled the witch, and she stuck her own head into the oven. Gretel gave her a great push and the witch fell in headlong. Then Gretel locked the door, and how the witch howled inside! But it served her right for she was a very wicked witch.

24th June

Hansel and Gretel (4)

Gretel quickly fetched the key to Hansel's cage and set him free. Then they ran back to the witch's house, where they found much treasure, gold, pearls and precious stones. They took as much as they could carry and set off home. They came to a big lake and they didn't know how to get over. Then along came a duck and carried them over one by one. The children thanked her very much, and soon the wood became more and more familiar to them, and in the end they saw their home.

The children began to run and they burst into the room where their father was sitting, full of sorrow. Their mother had just died, and there he sat, thinking about his lost children. They threw their arms around him then showed him their treasure. Now they were rich and no longer had to live in poverty. Father and children now live happily together, never to part again.

25th June

The Pixies in Devon (1)

What a life in Devon before,
With pixie-men to do your chores!
Then you could sit upon a bank,
And twiddle your thumbs until the sun sank.
With washing and scrubbing,
And cleaning and ironing,
And plucking and picking,
And polishing and running,
Before the rising of the sun,
There's your work already done.

Chambermaids snoozing deep in a chair,
Left the beds just lying there.
Meanwhile come the little men,
And make the rooms all tidy again.

With brushing and sweeping,
And dusting and washing,
And plumping and pulling,
And scrubbing and rushing,
Before the master blinked an eye,
There were the rooms all clean and dry.

The Butcher had a lazy life,
Still asleep there with his wife,
In come the elfs with running feet,
And chop and cut the heavy meat.
With hacking and chopping,
And cutting and pulling,
And measuring and piling,
And panting and groaning,
When the Butcher finally wakes,
The meat is ready and waiting to take.

26th June

Pixies in Devon (2)

Mr. Baker didn't need,
To try too hard his customers to feed.
His lazy workers slept in flour,
While the pixies baked bread hour by
hour.
With kneading and thumping,
And rolling and sprinkling,
And humping and heating,
And sweating and grunting,
Still the workers deep in snores,
There the bread stood by the door.

27th June

Pixies in Devon (3)

At the brewery it was so,
The wine-brewer drank until he sank low
Into drunken dreams and happy snores,
While Pixies run in through the door.
With crushing and pressing,
And testing and sucking,
And wheeling and sinking,
And pouring and splashing,
Before the brewer with headache woke
up,
The wine was made and ready to sup.

Once the tailor had a worry,
For he was in a frightful hurry,
To make the new robe for the King,
So while he slept, the elves ran in.
With cutting and tearing,
And sewing and patching,
And fastening and fitting,
And knitting and stitching,
When the tailor woke and stared,
There was the ready robe lying there.

Oh dear! And now they're all away,
The people can no longer play.
They cannot leave work on the shelf,
But must get up early and do it
themselves!
With scratching and scraping,
And running and trotting,
And dressing and ironing,
And knocking and hacking,
And cooking and baking.
If only the little men would come!
Life really is no longer fun!

28th June

Pixies in Devon (4)

Curious was the tailor's wife,
And wanted to see them in real life,
She sprinkled peas upon the stairs,
And the pixies didn't see them there.
With tumbling and falling,
And shouting and bumping,
And slipping and sliding,
And knocking and bumping,
The little men had had enough!
The humans were lazy and too rough!

29th June

The Silly Little Goose (1)

You see the silly little goose that's poking his head out of the cage? Well, that's me! Well it *was* me, I'm not so stupid anymore, I've learned a lot. That picture shows me on my first journey — my family were taken to another farm. Mum was afraid I'd hit my head against something. On the farm I was very vain. Every time I found a caterpillar, I wrapped it round me as a fur coat and waddled off to the pond to look at myself. Our cock

116

as also angry with me, for I pulled one of his feathers out for my hat. One day when I was admiring myself in the cellar window, I heard my mother explaining to my sisters how to make a nest. "Let them learn it," I thought, "I'm not interested! But when my mother noticed I wasn't there, I got a good box on the ears. Then one day a suitor came and wanted to marry me, but I gave his flowers to the goat, who ate them. The poor suitor flew away.

told me later. The animals fetched the farmer's gun and shot the fox. I was freed! All the other geese were freed too. My suitor still wanted to marry me and I was glad. All the animals were very nice to me, and I was no longer so proud!

1st July

A Dear Little Sunny Ray

The sunny ray so brightly shines,
For now it's really summertime,
Children swimming, oh so merry,
Are looking as bronzed as a summer berry.
See the sailing ships on the waves,
Goldly tipped by the sunny rays.
From the white sand finely ground,
You can see mountains hover around.

30th June

The Silly Little Goose (2)

Mum was so annoyed that I was so badly brought up, but I didn't listen to her. Then I met a fox. He was very handsome and told me many tales about the wood.

The fox kept telling me how pretty I was, but as I looked in the mirror, I saw lots of little geese tied up behind me. I was terrified and ran away, but the fox ran after me and wasn't so friendly anymore. He snapped me up between his teeth, and I don't know what happened after that for I fainted. But the little bird who ran back to the farm and raised the alarm

2nd July

The Story of Elsie (1)

Elsie still felt terribly unhappy at the boarding school, although she had been there for three weeks. She wrote a long, unhappy letter to her father. The worst thing for her was that she had to obey strict rules, whereas at home she had been able to do what she wanted. Every Wednesday she had to knit, even though she couldn't do it. One day Miss Ray asked to see what she had done, but Elsie pretended she hadn't heard, so Miss Ray took it from her. When she showed the

other girls Elsie's untidy mess, they laughed, and Elsie shook with anger. Scarcely was Miss Ray out of the room when Elsie threw her knitting against the wall, and she demanded to be sent home straight away. Miss Gus and Nellie could hardly calm her down, and they tried to tell her that she had done wrong and should apologise. Later Elsie knocked at Miss Ray's door, and for the first time in her life, stammering and sobbing, she said the word, "Sorry."

3rd July

The Story of Elsie (2)

It was autumn, and Nellie saw that the apples on the trees outside her window were ripe.

Unfortunately, it was forbidden to pick them. Elsie told Nellie how at home she used to climb up the tree and pick them, so both girls made a plan. At night when everyone was asleep, Elsie was to climb the tree and pick some apples. Elsie was pleased because that meant she could wear her old blue dress again. When she was climbing the tree she felt indescribably happy – it was just like being at home again. Through the windows she could see her friends asleep in bed. Nellie was terrified she would get caught, and then they would both be sent home, but Elsie was enjoying her new freedom. At home when she was climbing trees, her father would always call up to her, "Yahoo!" and Elsie just couldn't stop herself from shouting out "Yahoo!" now at the top of her voice. All the lights in the house were on straight away, and Elsie tried to climb back into the room as quickly as she could, helped by Nellie, pale as death. Elsie jumped into bed fully clothed and pulled the covers up to her chin. Miss Ray came into the room and asked, "Didn't you hear the shout?" Nellie pretended to be very surprised, and Elsie pretended to be asleep.

Luckily Miss Ray didn't notice Elsie's boots in the bed. Nellie heaved a sigh of relief and bit into one of the apples, but Elsie didn't dare get out of bed again.

The days went by and soon it was Christmas. Elsie and her friends decorated the Christmas tree, and everyone was looking forward to the presents they would get – everyone except Nellie. She had no family, and no

one who thought about her. But on Christmas Day there was also a present for her – from Elsie's parents. Nellie was overjoyed.

4th July

The Story of Elsie (3)

Elsie had at last settled in at the boarding school. She won many friends, but Nellie was the best! In January a dancing class began for the young ladies, but the first lesson they didn't enjoy at all, for no men were yet allowed, and they had to dance together. But one day Miss Ray informed them that tonight men would be coming to the class. The young ladies were so excited that they took hours to get ready, what with washing and combing their hair and making themselves look beautiful. When they were ready, they stood outside the room hardly daring to go in.

But from now on the dancing lessons were much more fun than before, and after four weeks there was to be a ball. Everyone took great trouble in getting ready. Nellie and Elsie had been given material by Elsie's parents, and they

made themselves new Ball gowns. "How beatiful you look," said Lillie, the youngest girl in the school. She was very excited, for she was allowed to go too. The older girls were no less excited, for it was their first Ball. Miss Ray had invited some more guests, and an Orchestra.

The girls had decorated the Ballroom with bright lanterns, and the long dresses of the girls with the dark suits of the men made the Ball look really official. Miss Gus looked at Elsie with joy – out of the wild stubborn child of before had grown a charming young girl.

5th July

The Story of Elsie (4)

Because of her friendly, natural way, Elsie had become very popular, among the men too. Elsie often thought how she must have hurt her mother, and one day she sat down and wrote a letter of apology. Then she waited impatiently for the reply. Miss Ray read all the letters, and she told Elsie that of course her mother had forgiven her.

But the best news of all was that now Elsie had a little baby brother! Elsie threw her arms around Miss Ray's neck. Now she couldn't wait to go home to see her little brother. But at the moment the girls were doing a play, and Elsie was playing the part of a girl who was wild and stubborn – you can imagine why she had that part! Now Elsie could put on her old blue dress again, even though it was too small now. When the play was performed, Elsie was the star of the show. The audience were fascinated with her. But now it really was time to leave, and Elsie saw Nellie cry for the first time. She was heartbroken at having to leave her friend. "It's not for ever!" comforted Elsie. Then one of the other girls said: "Let's promise to meet here again after exactly three years!" Everyone made a solemn promise.

The Story of Elsie (5)

The day of departure had come, and although Elsie was looking forward to seeing her family, she was very sad at having to leave her friends and the place that had been her home for a whole year.

She told Nellie to visit her as often as she could. "How lonely I'll be without you!" sobbed Nellie. All her friends brought her flowers, and she put them all in a basket in her lap. Miss Gus and Nellie took her to the station, and after they had said

goodbye for the last time, Elsie sped off in the train. In the train she remembered how wretched she had felt when she first came. She had never believed she would be so sorry to leave. The lady sitting opposite on the train tried to comfort her, but she could not cheer up until she saw her father standing on the platform. She threw her arms around him and then embraced her mother and new little brother who had also come to meet her. She was filled with joy. "How big you've grown!" exclaimed her father. "When you went away you were just a child, but now! . . . I can hardly believe it!" Mrs.

Macket was happy that Elsie had finally accepted her. Elsie put her arms around her and said: "Mama, dear Mama!" That said it all. Above the door at home was a big sign saying "Welcome," and Bob the dog ran to greet her. The whole house was decorated.

But Elsie just couldn't take her attention from the baby, and she danced around the room with him until he started to cry, and then she had to lay him in his little cot. But there was yet another surprise for Elsie. Her room had been completely newly decorated, and at the window stood an easel, for in the boarding school she had discovered her great talent for drawing, and her parents wanted to encourage this talent. Then one day Elsie got a letter from Nellie, that told her she had got engaged. Nellie as a bride! But Mrs. Macket smiled – Elsie had also become a young lady!

7th July

Rascals

The cock said to the hen: "The nuts are ripe, let's go up the mountain and eat our

fill before the squirrels eat them all!" So up they went, and because it was a nice day, they stayed until evening. Now whether it was because they were too far or too lazy, they decided they didn't want to walk home, so the hen had to make a car out of nutshells. "You can pull the car!" said the hen to the cock. "I'd rather walk than pull the cart," said the cock.

As they were arguing, along came a duck who said to them, "You thieves! Who said you could come onto my mountain and take my nuts? You just wait!" And she set on the cock. But the cock fought back, and with one particularly hard peck, the duck fell to the floor and begged for mercy, and as punishment, she let herself be harnessed to the cart. The cock sat on the cart as the driver and whipped the duck into running. As they were going along, they met two pedestrians, a needle and a pin. "Stop, stop!" they called. Soon it would be dark and they wouldn't be able to see anymore, couldn't they ride with them? They were staying in the tailor-hostel and they had to get there before it closed. Because they were only thin and wouldn't take up much room, the cock let them get in, but they had to promise not to tread on his or the hen's toes. Late in the evening they came to an inn, and because they didn't want to drive at night, they decided to stay there. The innkeeper wasn't too keen, for the inn was full, and they didn't look like a very honest group! But when they promised him the egg the hen had laid on the way, and that he could keep the duck who laid one every day, he said they could stay.

Early in the morning, when everyone was still asleep, the cock woke the hen, took the egg and pecked it, ate it, and threw the shell onto the fire. Then they got the needle, and stuck it in the innkeeper's cushion, while the pin they stuck in his towel, and then they flew away over the moor. The duck, who liked sleeping in the open air, heard them fly off, so he got up and swam off down the stream. A few hours later, the innkeeper got up, washed and dried himself on the towel, but the pin ran all over his face and cut him from ear to ear. Then he went into the kitchen and wanted to light his pipe in the fire, but the eggshell jumped into his eyes, "I'm not having much luck today!" he said, and sat wearily down in his armchair, but he didn't stay there long! "Ow!" he screamed, for the needle had wounded him in a much more painful place than his head! Now he was furious, and suspected those rough-looking guests he had allowed to stay.

But when he went to look for them they had gone. Now he swore that never again would he allow such rascals into his house, who took everything but paid for it only with dirty tricks!

8th July

Little Red Riding Hood (1)

There was once a little girl who was so sweet and nice that everyone loved her. She was loved most of all by her grandmother. One day her grandmother gave the little girl a red velvet hood, and she liked it so much that she would never wear another one. Soon everyone started to call her, "Little Red Riding Hood." One day her mother gave the

little girl a basket with cakes and wine to take to her grandmother for she was i "But don't wander from the path," he mother warned, "for in the wood ther are many dangers!" Because he grandmother lived quite a long way from the village, Little Red Riding Hood set o straight away. Then in the wood she m the wolf: "Good morning, Little Re Riding Hood," he said politely. "Wher are you off to so early?" Little Red Ridin Hood didn't know what a wicked anim the wolf was, and so she replied: "I' taking cake and wine to my granny."
"Where does your grandmother live? asked the wolf. "In the middle of th wood under the three big oak trees, replied the girl innocently. Then the wo thought of a way he could catch Little Re Riding Hood and her grandmother. Fu of cunning he said to the girl: "Aren't th flowers lovely! I bet your grandmothe would love a bunch!" "What a goo idea!" said Little Red Riding Hood, an although she had promised not t wander from the path, she ran into th forest and picked some flower

Meanwhile the wolf went straight to grandmother's house. He knocked on the door and said: "It's me, Little Red Riding Hood!" "Ah, come in!" said granny. The wolf crept to granny's bed and swallowed her whole. Then he put on her nightcap got into bed, and waited.

9th July

Little Red Riding Hood (2)

Meanwhile Little Red Riding Hood had picked so many flowers she could hardly carry them, and then she hurried to granny's. When she went into her granny's house, she took one look at her and said, "Granny, what big ears you have!" "All the better to hear you with!" replied the wolf.

"But, granny, what big eyes you have!" wondered Little Red Riding Hood.

"All the better to see you with!" replied the wolf.

"Hey, granny, what big hands you have!" "All the better to hold you with!" said the wolf.

"But what big teeth you have!" cried Little Red Riding Hood, who was now afraid.

"All the better to eat you with!" growled the wolf, and he sprang out of bed and swallowed her! He got back into bed, fell asleep and snored enough to shake the walls. Meanwhile it had turned midday, and the hunter was coming home for lunch, and when he went past granny's house, he said to himself, "Why is the old lady snoring so loud? I'd better go and see if she's alright. When he went in and saw the wolf in bed, he was very shocked. And because he thought the wolf must have eaten granny, he didn't shoot him, but carefully cut open his stomach. After he had made a few cuts, Little Red Riding Hood jumped out, closely followed by grandmother, who was still alive but who could hardly breathe. Little Red Riding Hood danced for joy around the room, and then she fetched some stones and filled the wolf's stomach with them.

When he woke up and wanted to run away, the stones were so heavy that he fell dead on the floor. All three were very relieved, and they all sat down and ate the cakes and wine. But Little Red Riding Hood thought, "I'll never wander from the path or disobey mummy again!"

123

Night-time

The sun would like to sleep now,
She's had a busy day,
Already the moon is pushing,
Her golden face away.

The sparrows in the forest,
Are sleeping in their nests,
And even the sprightly squirrel
Has closed his door to rest.

But for the big-eyed wise owl,
And the little shy field-mouse,
The day is just beginning,
And they hover round your house.

The nightingale is singing,
A lullaby in your tree,
The croaking frogs jump from their
ponds,
At night time they are free!

The stars are smiling brightly,
In the night-time sky so dark,
The cat squeals on the tiles,
And the dogs begin to bark.

The gentle deer goes grazing,
Upon the meadow grass,
But the prickly hedgehog's dreaming,
Of a happy day that's passed.

The little rabbit's sleeping,
Where no sly fox can see,
And the sailing boats are bobbing,
On the waves out on the sea.

So sleep now, little children,
Like the taverns in the town,
And the hedgehogs, birds and sunshine,
On the softest feather down.

A Tale of Ducks

Once, when hunting, I saw some duck
who unfortunately were too far away o
the lake. This meant that I could on
shoot one, and I only had one shot left. S
I took a piece of ham, tied it onto a strin
which I cast out like a fishing rod and hi
Soon a duck came along and swallowe
the string as well as the ham. Then eac
of the ducks took hold of the strin
hoping to drag the ham from the duck
mouth. Soon I had them all on the line
had to tie the string around my body fo
the birds were madly flapping the
wings, but soon they managed to fly o
into the air, dragging me up with them
used my rifle as a rudder and steere
them towards my house, where we fle
in down the chimney and landed on th
fireplace!

12th July

Jumbolino (1)

Once, in deepest Africa, there stood an elephant, alone and deserted. His mother had been captured during a big game-hunt, but he had managed to run away into the jungle. You can imagine how frightened he was now, alone in the jungle without his mother. He cried big elephant tears. But all the other animals in the jungle were afraid of him.

For although he was so young, he was much bigger than they. Once when he turned around, he saw five little coloured children staring at him in amazement. Although they too were afraid of him, the youngest one went up to him and said: "You look so sad! Come and play with us." The elephant was overjoyed, took all the little children on his back and carried them to their hut. They lived by a river, and what fun they had there! They ran around and played from morning till night.

13th July

Jumbolino (2)

Jumbolino was very happy with the children, but one day when they were bathing in the river, big game-hunters came by and caught the elephant. The children were very angry and decided to follow the waggon and free Jumbolino. They followed it to the sea, and far out on the water stood Jumbolino on a sailing ship. The children swam out to it and stowed away on board. The ship had only sailed for a few days when it ran into a storm and sank. Jumbolino and the children clung onto a log and were saved, and the log sailed off to a little island. How happy they all were there! When the storm died down, they brought everything they could save from the sea onto the shore.

Then they went exploring, and they certainly couldn't have found a better home if they'd tried! First of all they built themselves a new hut that could protect them from any storm. When the hut was finished, they were so tired they all lay down and went to sleep. The next day they had a big party to celebrate their survival. They danced and sang and drank sweet palm wine. They had never been so happy. In the evenings, when the moon shone, they would sit on the beach and stare out onto the wide sea, rejoicing over their new home.

14th July

Berry-picking

Who are they disappearing into the wood? It's shopkeeper Hemmings, and Mary and Rose from the farm. "Most of the bilberries grow by the pond," says Mr. Hemmings. He remembers from last year. But Rose thinks that most grow in the clearing. Mary humms a tune — it's all the same to her where they look. And Strubble the dog barks, just to say that he loves it here in the wood.

They don't have to go much further, for soon they catch sight of the red and black berries shining in front of them, and they set to work picking.

Before long the baskets are half full, but they loaded even more into their mouths! Now they're tired and hungry, and they sit down on the heather and eat their sandwiches. Strubble had already fallen asleep, but later they carry on picking until their baskets are completely full. Then they start for home, but they'll be back tomorrow, and the next day, and every day, until the berry season is over.

15th July

Luggage

A lady travelled down to Harwich,
With lots of luggage in her carriage,
A basket, a case, a travelling bag,
A hat-box, a cushion, a doll called Mag,
A bucket, a table, a fancy dish,
A doll's house, a fireplace, a rubber fish,
Four boxes lying on a log,
And a little red-ribboned barking dog.

The driver looked at her with a frown,
For all these things would weigh them
down,
The basket, the case, the travelling bag,
The hat-box, the cushion, a doll called
Mag,
The bucket, the table, the fancy-dish,
The doll's house, the fireplace, the rubber
fish,
Four boxes lying on a log,
And the little red-ribboned barking dog.

The little dog sat down and howled,
At all these things he madly growled,
At the basket, the case and the travelling
bag,
At the hat-box, the cushion, the doll
called Mag,
At the bucket, the table and the fancy
dish,
At the doll's house, the fireplace and the
rubber fish,
Four boxes lying on a log,
Full of fear away ran the dog.

Luckily upon the scene,
Appeared the dog with skin so lean,
With the basket, the case and the
travelling bag,
With the hat-box, the cushion, the doll
called Mag,
With the bucket, the table and facy dish,
With the doll's house, the fireplace and
rubber fish,
With the four boxes lying on a log,
There was now this skinny dog.

When in Harwich she wanted to see,
What the worth of this luggage could be,
Of the basket, the case and the travelling
bag,
Of the hat-box, the cushion and the doll
called Mag,
Of the bucket, the table and fancy dish,
Of the doll's house, the fireplace and
rubber fish,
Four boxes lying on a log,
But not the dirty skinny dog.

The keeper said, "You've kept them well,
All these things should quickly sell,
The basket, the case and the travelling-
bag,
The hat-box, the cushion, the doll called
Mag,
The bucket, the table, the fancy dish,
The doll's house, the fireplace, the rubber
fish,
Four boxes lying on a log,
But not this worthless skinny dog!"

16th July

The Snowman in Summer

Do you see the funny snowman here? His
hat is an old bowler, his nose is a carrot,
and his eyes are two pieces of coal. Do
you want to have a snowman too? Then

come into the garden, John will show you how to build one. But winter is over, and snowdrops are already blooming, the snowman stands sad and deserted by the garden wall. Through sheer loneliness he catches a fever, and day and night he dreams of going on a summer journey. He longs for summer, just like the children, and because he wants it so much, he begins to walk! How the people stare as he happily plods through the streets. Our snowman wonders over the flowers on the meadow and the trees, but how the sun hurts! Quickly he makes a sunshade out of leaves. "Now the sun can't hurt me!" he thinks, and he happily walks on. But

high in the sky, the sun causes the snowman to sweat terribly, and thick drops of moisture run down his face. The sun also causes his shade to wilt. When the ice-cream man sees the snowman, he feels sorry for him and gives him a strawberry ice-cream. He soon gulps it down!

Then our snowman goes to visit the Polar-bear in the zoo, for he thinks that he surely won't sweat there. But it's just as bad here, and his fever gets worse. Then he meets an ice-skater from the Ice Revue, who invites him to a performance. The snowman likes it very much, and he has a go too, but soon he carries on walking and wanders to the wood. The sun still beats down without pity, and the snowman begins to melt. Soon, when he is no bigger than a doll, he flees into the shadows of a bush. A little girl finds him there, and she dresses him up as a bridegroom and marries him to her doll. She puts them both in their wedding carriage and takes them home. There, in the garden, a few curious sunrays shine on him, and he melts and melts until all that's left is a bowler hat, a carrot and two pieces of coal. So that was the end of the snowman's summer journey. The little girl was amazed when she came back and found her handsome Snowman gone! Where had he gone?

17th July

Cinderella (1)

There was once a rich man who had lived happily with his wife for many years, and they had one daughter.

Then his wife fell ill, and on her death bed she called the daughter to her and said: "My dear child, I have to leave you, but I shall watch over you from Heaven. Plant a tree by my grave, and whenever you want anything, just shake it and your wish shall be granted." Then she died. The child cried and cried, but did as her mother had told her. The snow laid a white cloth over her mother's grave, and

The ugly sisters called for Cinderella: "Comb our hair, brush our shoes and help us dress. We're going to the King's Ball." Cinderella would have loved to go, but her step-mother said: "I have poured a bowl of lentils into the ashes, if you can pick them out within two hours, then you can come!" Cinderella went out the back door and summoned all the doves and turtle doves to help her sort the lentils. In they flew one by one, and within an hour the lentils stood in a dish. She went back to her stepmother, but she was not a woman of her word, and she said to Cinderella: "You can't dance and you haven't anything to wear, you would put us to shame. Come, daughters!" And they hurried off to the ball. Cinderella rushed into the garden and shook the tree by her mother's grave. There, before her, appeared an old lady. "I am your fairy godmother!" she said. "Fetch me a pumpkin and seven mice, and you shall go to the ball!" Cinderella rushed to the kitchen and fetched a pumpkin and called out the mice who were all her friends.

by the time it had melted, her father had married again. This woman already had two proud, ugly daughters, and they were jealous of their stepsister. They took all her clothes away and made her wear an old grey skirt, then they dragged her down to the kitchens and made her work there from then on. She had to get up early, light the fire, cook and wash, and above all bear the mockery of her sisters. She had no bed, but had to sleep among the ashes in the fireplace, and because of this, they called her Cinderella.

18th July

Cinderella (2)

It came to pass that the King was to throw a ball that was to last three days, and all the young girls in the land were invited, so that the Prince could find himself a bride.

The fairy turned the pumpkin into a fine carriage and the mice into seven footmen. Then she gave Cinderella a silver dress and dainty glass slippers for her feet. "Be sure you are home by midnight," warned her grandmother, "for then the spell is over and everything will change back to its original form." Cinderella rode off in her carriage and was the belle of the ball. The Prince danced with no one else but her the whole night. Her stepmother and sisters didn't recognise her in her fine clothes. Shortly before midnight Cinderella told the Prince that she must go, and although he tried to hold her back, she ran out of the ballroom, and no one knew where she went.

Cinderella (3)

All that night the Prince couldn't sleep, he had to find out who the strange lady was with whom he had danced. When the ugly sisters got home, there was Cinderella asleep in the ashes. The next day, when she asked her sisters about the ball, they said: "Oh, the Prince only had eyes for one girl, no one knows who she is. I hope she's not there tonight!"
That night Cinderella helped her sisters get ready, and as soon as they had gone, her fairy godmother appeared.
Again she turned the pumpkin into a carriage and the mice into footmen, then she gave Cinderella an even more beautiful dress. When she appeared at the Ball, her beauty took everyone's breath away. The Prince was delighted that his mysterious partner was there again, and he immediately took her by the hand and danced with her all night. But shortly before midnight she hurried out and back to her carriage. The Prince followed her and searched desperately for her in the gardens, but she was nowhere to be seen.

Cinderella (4)

On the third night, after her sisters had gone, her fairy godmother appeared again, and this time she gave Cinderella the most beautiful dress you can imagine. It was made of gold, studded with precious jewels, and when she put it on she shone like the sun when it is in its highest point in the sky. When she went into the Ballroom, everyone was dumbstruck by her beauty, and the ugly sisters were filled with envy. The Prince was enchanted and danced with no one else but her. This time shortly before midnight, the Prince held her close and would not let her go. The hands moved closer towards midnight.

When Cinderella finally got away she had to run as fast as she could, and in her haste she lost one of her glass slippers on the stairs. When the Prince ran after her, the glass slipper was all he found. The Prince let it be known that he would search for the person whose foot fitted this slipper, and whoever it belonged to would be his wife.

Cinderella (5)

The Prince rode around the Kingdom for many days, but the dainty little slipper was much too small for anyone. Then it was the turn of the ugly sisters. The first sister took the slipper into her room with her mother and tried it on, but she couldn't fit in her big toes.

Her mother said, "Squeeze your toes tighter. Force your foot in," and the sister hobbled out to the Prince. The Prince however saw the great pain on the ugly sister's face and knew this was not his lady. He gave the slipper to the other sister, but when she tried on the shoe, she could not fit in her heels. Her mother told her to force the shoe over her heel with a shoe horn. The sister pushed and pulled at the shoe and tried to force her heel into the little slipper. When she had finished, her heel was so sore she needed a walking stick to help her walk back to the Prince. The Prince knew this could not be his loved one. "Haven't you got any other daughters?" asked the Prince in despair, for there were no ladies left to try. "There's only Cinderella in the kitchens, but she didn't even go the Ball!" said Cinderella's father. The Prince, however, insisted that he should see her, and when Cinderella tried on the slipper, her dainty foot easily slipped in. When the Prince looked at her he recognised his mysterious beauty, and he embraced her fondly. As he lifted her onto his mare and swept her away to his palace, he left behind the two ugly sisters screaming with jealousy and pain.

Pim the Gnome

There was once a little gnome called Pim, who had a very big cap. When he pulled this cap down to his toes, he became invisible. Pim lived with his mother under an old tree-root. One day his mother said to him, "Whatever you do, don't lose your cap!"

Sitting sadly on a tree-stump was Muck the squirrel. "My paw is caught in the crack," he wailed, "When the fox comes he will eat me!" After great struggling Pim managed to free the squirrel, and to say thank you, Muck let Pim ride on his back. What fun that was! "Don't jump about so much or I'll lose my cap that makes me invisible!" Pim said. An old sulky raven heard him say this and made up his mind to steal the cap. Before Pim knew what was happening, the raven had swept down and grabbed the cap with his beak. Pim was in despair: "Without my cap I'm lost!" he wiled. "Don't worry," comforted the squirrel, "I know where the raven's nest is. We'll get your cap back!" And they set off towards the raven's home. Meanwhile the raven had flown back to his nest, happy with his loot, but without help he couldn't put the cap on himself. So he flew to the owl and said, "Help me put on this cap, becuse it makes you invisible!" Now the raven shouldn't have said that for now the owl wanted it. "It belongs to me, to me!" shrieked the raven. "I want it!" screeched the owl, "You only stole it after all!" The whole wood was filled with the din. Meanwhile along came Muck and Pim, and of course now it was easy for them to find the cap. Muck ran up the tree and grabbed it, and the Owl and the raven were far too busy arguing to notice. Muck gave it back to Pim and told him to take more care of it in future!

cherry tree growing in its horns – it was the stag I'd lost before! I looked forward to my roast with cherry sauce!

24th July

The Pig's Excursion

A pig was tired of sweating,
In the summer barn,
So he picked his tail and feet up,
And bolted from the farm.
The farmer went to feed him,
But when he went inside,
He found the pig had vanished,
So in the yard he cried:
"Farmhands, dogs and milkmaids,
The pig has run away,
So go out now and find him!
Don't slumber in the hay!"
Now the pig, too fat to run far,
Was soon caught by the tail,
And through the yard they dragged him,
Til in the barn he wailed.
For freedom is a short thing,
For pigs especially,
So in the barn he sweated,
Never more to flee!

23rd July

The Stag with the Cherry Tree

Once I saw a wonderful stag, but I didn't have any bullets left. Quickly I took some powder and some cherry kernels and shot. I hit the animal, but he escaped. Once I chased a hare all day. Every time I sent my dog after him, the hare escaped. When the dog finally caught him, I was amazed! It had four legs like any other animal, but it also had four other legs on its back which it used whenever it got tired! Years later I shot at a stag with a

The Old Bus (1)

Again the old bus has good reason to complain. He's already completely full, and here comes the farmer Mr. Pluderback with a sack full of cabbages, and slumps down in the already full corridor. That's too much! With a spit and a rumble the bus shudders to a halt. The driver tries the ignition, but gets no sign of life. "That's it! She's had it now! I'm afraid we'll have to walk!" says the driver. Everyone grabs their things and sulkily sets off. Fat old farmer Plunderback grunts and groans under his heavy load. The now useless bus cries and cries. This has been his stretch for years, and he knows every tree and every hedge. Now who's going to drive the children punctually to school? And what about all the workers who want to get home in the evenings? Now he has to stand there deserted! But not for long! Along comes the tow truck, and after being attached, the old bus is on the move again. What fun it is to ride along without having to make any effort! But, oh dear, the nice journey soon comes to an end, for the truck takes him and dumps him at the car cemetery. Is this the end?!

The Old Bus (2)

But that wasn't the end! One day the Mayor drove past the graveyard and saw the old bus. "Look!" he said, 'We can do something with that bus. I've been looking for something like that for weeks. I wonder what the children will say!'' And sure enough a few days later, the tow truck came back and hooked itself to the old bus, and the Mayor led the way into the town – the bus was to become a new play area for the children, and the Mayor handed it over to them to do what they wanted with it. The children were overjoyed with it, and set straight to work, cleaning and painting it. Bob wanted it to be red, but Mary thought it should be yellow, so making sure that everyone was satisfied, they painted it red and yellow! It was the best looking bus in the world! How happy the bus is! Never again is he lonely, for he plays with the children every day and every day he travels to a new country. But its all free, for it is in the dreams of children!

Obstinate Bob

Bob is a lion cub. He is yellow and as soft as a water baby. He is the youngest of three and wants to do everything differently from them. Whenever his mother goes hunting for food, he is forbidden to leave the nest. But one day when she goes off, away he trots! But wait! What's that smell? Isn't it the smell of humans that his mother warned him about? His father was killed by them recently because he wasn't careful enough. But Bob is curious and he climbs onto a stone to see better. *Snap!* Something falls on top of him, a trap. He has fallen into a trap! Mother lion hears his cries and, furious, she runs over to him. Bob nearly faints with pain as his mother has to tear his ear out of the trap, because that's the only way to free him. Mother warns him once and for all never to leave the nest again, otherwise something even worse might happen. But Bob doesn't listen, and the next time he wanders off alone, he is caught by a lion hunter and all his cries this time are in vain. He is loaded onto a ship with other animals, and his cage is so small he can hardly move. He is bought by a Zoo, and his freedom is lost for ever.

Meanwhile he has grown into a big strong lion, but sometimes he feels so homesick he cries bitter tears. His regret is as big as his homesickness, but his regret has come too late. His mother had searched in vain for him for weeks until she heard from other lions what had happened to him. She cried for a long time, and her only comfort was that her other children were not so obstinate and listened to their mother.

Christopher and the Balloon (1)

Christopher was still very young. One day, when he was standing at the gate, he saw some children with a big red balloon, and he liked it so much that he wanted one too, but he didn't know where to get one. So he asked all the animals if they knew, but they shook their heads. Then the donkey said, "I know where to get one!" So Christopher jumped on his back, and the donkey trotted away to the annual market. Christopher climbed down and saw a man selling lots of balloons, but you had to pay for them. Christopher bent his head sadly for he didn't have any money. Then on the ground he saw a purse, and he quickly ran after the lady who must have dropped it. The lady was delighted and asked him what he would like Christopher replied that he would like to buy a candy heart for his mother and a sugar stick for his donkey. "Don't you want anything for yourself?" asked the lady. Christopher shook with excitement: "Oh yes, I'd so love a balloon!" The lady smiled and bought every balloon the man had! He thanked her very much and remembered his mother, who was probably wondering where he was, so he rushed to his donkey who took him home.

Christopher and the Balloon (2)

On the way home, Christopher was thinking how he couldn't wait to give his mother the candy heart. Meanwhile his mother had got very worried, for the cat had told her how Christopher had simply got on the donkey and rode off. When she saw him come back, really she should have scolded him, but she was so glad to see him that she gave him a big hug. How pleased she was with her candy heart! Then she wanted to know everything that had happened, and after Christopher had told her the whole story, she wrote it down on several little letters and tied each one to a balloon. Christopher was allowed to keep one of them, while they set the other ones free into the air.

How happy the children were who received one of these balloons. In it they read the story of "Christopher and the balloon", and each one wished that he could have an experience like that. Who knows? If everyone was as helpful and honest as Christopher, then maybe it would happen to them!

Boldi Becomes
a Television Star (1)

One day Tom and Boldi were watching television. The announcer of the childrens' hour said that for the next transmission some children were to come to her studio and show their favourite toys. Boldi and Tom were very excited and decided to go. Tom's mother sewed a new jacket for Boldi, and he danced around on the sewing machine in delight. The night before their outing they couldn't sleep at all, but soon the day had come. When they arrived at the studios, a friendly lady led them into a bright little room. Each was called in one by one, and when it was your turn, you disappeared behind a secret door. Then it was their turn! A man led them into another room and told Tom to sit down on a chair. Then he slapped make-up on his face, so that Tom wouldn't look too pale under the lights. When they both sat before the camera, they did their bit perfectly.

Tom told his stories about Boldi in such a lively and animated way, and Boldi was more amusing than he'd ever been before. The viewers at home were enchanted. Sometimes Boldi would stare so innocently into the camera that he made everyone's heart melt. Then he would start acting the fool again and make everyone laugh. Because everyone was so fascinated with them, they were allowed to stay in front of the cameras until the end of the programme, so that when it was over, both of them were very tired, for it's not so easy to be on television. However, they enjoyed it so much, and Tom's parents were so very proud of their son that night Tom slept all night with a smile on his face and with Boldi in his arms.

Boldi Becomes
a Television Star (2)

The next morning he got a letter from the studios which said: "Dear Tom and Boldi, we enjoyed your first appearance so much, that we would like to make a whole series with you. Your parents will have to sign the contract, and then you can come to the studios again next week." Everyone was so excited, especially Boldi, and thinking it was the day they should appear, ran into the studios. Tom searched for Boldi everywhere, but he was nowhere to be found. Tom's mother said: "Tom, if Boldi doesn't turn up, you'll have to go into the studios on your own and tell them what's happened." When the studio heard what had happened they were rather worried, but they decided that Tom would have to go in front of the camera on his own. Tom went out on the air and started telling the children what had happened, but scarcely had he begun when Boldi jumped down onto his lap from one of the lamps. Boldi told everyone how out of excitement he had come to the studios too early without waiting for Tom, but he promised that in future he wouldn't go anywhere without Tom. You can imagine how delighted everyone was with this programme!

1st August

The Dear Little Sunny Ray

It's August! How the sun laughs,
And now the harvest's here,
Just look at all the happiness
My smiles have brought all year.
The oats, the rye, the barley too,
Blow in the summer breeze,
And through the warm evenings,
I dart among the trees.
Touched with the lanterns' glint.

quite unusual for an elephant. His friend's name was Krishna. He was an Indian boy, and he lived with his parents in a jungle village. His job was to look after the water buffaloes by the lake, and it was there that Rani always came to visit him. But one day Rani was very worried, because there had been so much rain that the river had swelled and soon it would flood everything. Rani wanted to save his friend before he drowned. Rani knew where there was dry land, but he had to swim because the water was already deep. Much later on they came to a deserted town and there they stayed the night. They didn't wake up until the sun was already high in the sky.

2nd August

Rani and his Friend (1)

Rani was a young elephant who lived in the jungle. He had a real friend, which is

3rd August

Rani and his Friend (2)

When they looked around them, they saw a stone temple and old tumbledown houses. The inhabitants must have left many years ago, probably because they were afraid of a flood. Krishna found some fruit to eat and then they rode on. Towards evening they came to a big town. There the streets were very wide, and there were so many people you ouldn't possibly have counted them all. Dealers sat out on the streets under sunshades shouting out their bargains. Krishna would have loved to buy something, but he had no money. Suddenly in rushed a strange waggon, which although no oxen were attached to it could still move. Krishna had never seen a car before you see! Rani had never seen one either and so the pair of them ran away in fear. Soon they found

them. Then he had to tell them his story, after which the elephant was given hay and Rani a bed for the night. But when it was night, Krishna crept out to his elephant and undid him, for Rani didn't like being tied up. Together they plodded out of the town into the night, but by morning they reached the jungle village again. The water had withdrawn, and Krishna walked triumphantly back home. But he kept going down to the lake, for he had a friend there!

themselves in a narrow alley and they were lost, so Krishna climbed onto Rani's back and the elephant went to sleep, but the boy was too hungry to sleep. He could smell warm rice coming from a nearby house, and he shyly looked in through the window. When the family saw him and how hungry he looked, they waved him in and invited him to eat with

4th August

Annie and Bill

Annie has a goldfish called Bill. Annie is nine years old and the fish means everything to her. On a sunny morning during the holidays, Annie went to her friend Elsie's house straight after feeding the fish. Tired of playing with the dolls, they begin to play hide-and-seek. Elsie's brother joins in as well. Annie hides in a cupboard, and when she closes the door she locks herself in. It's so dark inside she can't see anything, and she begins to scream in fear as she thinks she'll never get out again. But Elsie's brother heard her screaming and opened the door from outside and comforted her. When she goes home, she stands dumbstruck at her bedroom door – there stands Lux, the big black cat, trying to fish Bill out of his bowl. Annie angrily chases the cat away and looks sadly at her fish: "Poor old Bill," she said, "Lux has been worrying you all this time and I didn't even know." Then she imagined herself in the place of the fish, and for a second she felt the terrible fear of being shut in a small place like that morning in the cupboard. She thought about the big fish pond in the park, and she decided to put her Bill in the pond. It wasn't easy to see him go, but he would certainly make a lot of friends there, for he was so sweet.

5th August

Puss in Boots (1)

Sitting together one fine evening were three miller's sons. The miller came and sat with them and said, "I won't live much longer, but you mustn't quarrel when I've gone, for I shall share out everything I have – my eldest son shall have the mule, the second the donkey and Michael, the youngest, shall have the cat." When the miller died, Michael said to the cat, "Whatever shall I do with you?" The cat purred, "Just give me a pair of boots and I'll make you a fine rich gentleman!" At first Michael laughed, but since the cat insisted he called the cobbler and had some boots made for the cat. The cat was very proud of them and one day when he was prancing around the marketplace he heard the farmer talking. He said that the royal cook had ordered some partridges from him, but he didn't have any and the King was

very angry. So the cat took a sack of corn and a rope and went into the wood. Above a certain patch of ground he suspended the sack and below the sack he scattered the corn. One bird after another came to eat the corn, and when there were seven birds on the patch, the cat let go of the rope and caught them. Then the cat went to the King. He bowed to the King in such an elegant way that the King was quite delighted. "I am the messenger of the Duke Michael of Michaelson and Millhouse-on-sea," said the cat. "As a sign of his respect he has sent you seven partridges!" "Partridges! It can't be true!" exclaimed the King, and he was so pleased that he gave the cat a sack of gold. Meanwhile the miller's son sat at home, despairing because he had spent his last money on the cat's boots. Then the door opened and in walked the cat with a sack. He opened it up and poured gold all over the floor.

6th August

Puss in Boots (2)

The miller's son was delighted with the treasure, but while the cat was pulling off his boots he said, "That's not all I can do for you! By the way, I've told the King you're a duke!" After that the cat really set to work and caught lots of booty in the wood – quails, partridges and pigeons – and he took them all to the King, who always paid him a princely sum for them. One day, while the cat was warming himself in front of the fire in the royal kitchens, the old carriage driver rushed in, grumbling, "Always rushing about! Today I've got to drive the King and the Princess down to the river for a walk!" On hearing this the cat slipped out of the kitchens and rushed home. "Today I'm going to make you a duke!" he panted, and he dragged Michael down to the river. Then the cat made him undress and get into the water and afterwards he hid Michael's clothes behind a bush. When

the King and his daughter came along in their carriage, the cat bounded up to it and pretended to be surprised to see the King there. "Your Majesty!" he exclaimed, "While my master was bathing someone stole his clothes and if he stays in the water much longer he'll freeze!" When the King heard this he sent someone back to the Palace to fetch some clothes. The young man dressed and when he stood before the Princess, she liked him immediately. The King, thinking this was the generous duke who kept sending him birds, invited him to get into the carriage.

7th August

Puss in Boots (3)

After his master had got into the carriage, the cat ran on ahead and he found some people working in a meadow. He said to them, "Who do these fields belong to?" "To the wizard," they replied. "Your King is passing by," said the cat, "and when he asks you who the fields belong to, tell him they belong to the duke. If you don't, you'll be sorry!"

Then the cat ran on further and he came to a cornfield. This field also belonged to the wizard, but the cat told the workers to say the same thing. Then he walked on and came to the wizard's wood, but he told the woodcutters to say it belonged to the duke. Soon the cat reached a great castle. The cat fearlessly walked in, even though he knew it belonged to the wizard. When he encountered the wizard, he greeted him with a fine bow. "Most honourable wizard," he said "I hear you are an outstanding magician and can turn yourself into any kind of animal,

141

except for an elephant, of course." "Of course I can turn myself into an elephant!" exclaimed the wizard, and after a big puff of smoke, there stood a huge elephant. "My word!" exclaimed the cat, "If you could only turn yourself into a tiny mouse I'd say you were the best magician in the world!" "I *am* the best magician in the world!" exclaimed the wizard, and after another puff of smoke, there stood a tiny mouse. In a flash the cat had grabbed it and gobbled it down! That was the end of the wicked wizard!

8th August

Puss in Boots (4)

While the cat was getting rid of the wizard, the King, the Princess and Michael were still riding along. When they came to the meadow, the King asked, "Who does this meadow belong to?" And the people replied, "It belong to the Duke." The same happened at th cornfield and at the wood. The King said "You must be a very rich man, Duk Michael, even I haven't got this muc land!" When they came to the big castle the King's mouth dropped open wit surprise when the cat came down th stairway and said, "Would your Majest do Duke Michael the honour of visitin his castle?" After having seen all thi wealth, the King was of the same mind a his daughter and, of course, the cat ha thought of it first – the King gav Michael his daughter as a bride, an when the King died Michael inherited hi Kingdom. The cat, of course, becam Minister and his opinion was alway asked on the most important matters, fo he was the cleverest in the land. The ca was overjoyed to see his master and hi pretty wife so happy, and proud that h also enjoyed the greatest honour an respect.

9th August

When the Day is Over

When the day is over,
The dark wind whistles by,
The sun sinks low down in the west,
And the sky begins to cry.
So go to sleep, my little child,
Don't look out at the world so wild.

10th August

The Three Wishes

There was once a young couple who were very happy together, but they had one fault, which is the fault of all mankind - the more they had the more they wanted. One evening as they were sitting happily by the fire, a tiny white lady came in. She said to them, "I am your friend, a mountain-fairy, and I live in the crystal castle in the hills. I have chosen to give you three wishes, any wish you have shall be fulfilled, but I warn you! You have one week to make your wishes in — think carefully and don't be too hasty." Then she disappeared. The couple were so excited, and they tried to think what to use their wishes on, but they thought they had plenty of time to decide. Then the next evening, as they were waiting for the potatoes to boil, joyfully thinking about their future happiness, the lovely smell of the potatoes rose to Lisa's nostrils and she said, "Oh! I wish we had a lovely big sausage to go with them!" Oh dear! Their first wish had been used up! There lay a big fat sausage on top of the potatoes! Her husband was so angry at her carelessness that he cried, ".I wish it had grown on your nose, you stupid woman!" Oh dear! Now the big fat sausage was stuck on Lisa's nose! They only had one wish left and of course they had to use it up getting rid of this sausage. When they had made the wish they sat down and looked at each other sadly. Now they still only had what they had had before and the mountain fairy never came back.

11th August

Hubbi the Happy Helicopter

Dear children, in the next few days we will be telling you the adventures of Hubbi the helicopter. We hope you enjoy them!

Hubbi and the Blackbirds

Hubbi is a little helicopter. With the help of his propellors he can fly into the sky and either keep quite still or fly backwards. Just out of the town stands his little house. One morning along comes a blackbird. "Quick, Hubbi!" it calls in a panic, "You've got to help me! Follow me to my nest!" When Hubbi gets there, he finds two woodcutters cutting down the tree, and the young chicks are chirping in terror. So Hubbi flies right up to the tree while mother blackbird picks them all up one by one and loads them into the helicopter. They're saved! The blackbirds sing Hubbi a song to show their gratitude.

12th August

Hubbi and the Chimney-Sweep

While flying alone one day, Hubbi saw a town, and sitting on a roof he saw a chimney-sweep looking as though he was going to burst out crying.
"Are you so tired?" asked Hubbi. "I've an idea, tie your broom to my door and climb up!" With Hubbi's help the sweeping became childsplay, for the broom was put into the chimney and Hubbi just kept moving up and down! When they'd finished, Hubbi asked the sweep for a favour, and away they flew to Hubbi's house and cleaned his chimney

until it was cleaner than ever before. But Hubbi's tank was getting emptier and emptier, so he had to go to a petrol station to fill his tank. The petrol men were astonished when they saw Hubbi landing, for it's not every day you get a helicopter as a customer! The men filled Hubbi's tank and also tested the brakes. Hubbi politely thanked the men and did a lap of honour around the station, but it wasn't long before all you could hear was the humming of his engine.

13th August

Hubbi and Ellen's Suitcase

On the edge of the town is the railway station. The train has just left, but on the platform stands Mrs. Simpson with a suitcase, looking very upset. When she saw Hubbi she said, "I've just sent my little daughter Ellen on holiday to her

Aunty Eva and she was in such a hurry she forgot her suitcase. What on earth shall I do?

But of course Hubbi knew what to do. "Just put it in my luggage compartment and I'll sort it out for you!" Ellen had already missed her case when she saw Hubbi fly past the window. "Oh thank you, Hubbi!" she said, "Whatever would I have done without my nightie and suitcase?"

14th August

Hubbi and the Laundry Woman

Outside the town lies Mrs. Miller's laundry. Hubbi lands on the meadow. "Good day, Mrs. Miller," says Hubbi. "Good day, Hubbi!" says Mrs. Miller, "How nice of you to visit me. Where are you off to?" "To visit my friends the blackbirds!" "You little ragamuffin," laughs Mrs. Miller, "you can't go visiting looking that!" She already had her scrubbing-brush out and soon she had scrubbed Hubbi until he shone. "I wish my washing would dry!" she said, "But there's no wind today!" Then Hubbi had an idea, and he had Mrs. Miller hang her washing on his propellors and – wish! – the washing's soon dry.

15th August

Hubbi Helps the Police

After that Hubbi sets off to visit the blackbirds, who have settled into their new home very well. The little birds had already learned to fly and they flew excitedly towards Hubbi when they saw him coming. After having spent a very pleasant evening with them he went home. Because he's happy, he puts on his earphones to listen to the radio, but suddenly the music stops. "Attention please! Attention please! This is the Police! A red car has just been stolen and the thief is escaping. Citizens are asked to help the police in their investigations." Up in the air Hubbi has an excellent view, and he searches carefully below him.

There! A red car racing northwards!

Hubbi gets through on his radio to the Police: "I have discovered a suspicious car — send reinforcements northwards over and out — Hubbi!" Meanwhile, Hubbi catches the car up, and when she realises she's being followed, she accelerates. But Hubbi lets down a rope with a strong hook on the end and he attaches it to the car's back bumper. It lifts the car off the ground and Hubbi holds it there until the police arrive and arrest the thieves. Hubbi modestly flies away when the police try to thank him. He flies off to seek new adventures.

16th August

The Mouse in the Cake (1)

Once upon a time a mouse went past a baker's and looked in through the window. What a wonderful sight! Now he noticed how his tummy was rumbling and so he secretly slipped into the shop. Soon he started licking greedily at a big cream cake, and because it tasted so

lovely, the mouse licked himself right inside the cake and only his long tail could be seen. Then an old lady came into the shop and couldn't resist the sight of this very cake. "Ooh! I'll have four slices of that one!" she said. But just as the baker was about to cut the cake, the mouse stuck out its little head. The woman screamed, and the baker, in his shock, slammed his fist down into the cake so that the cream flew into his face and all over the lady's clothes. But the little mouse escaped.

17th August

The Mouse in the Cake (2)

The little mouse ran into the baking room, followed by the baker wiping the cream from his eyes. He saw the mouse's tail in the flour where the mouse had hidden himself. He made a grab at it, but only caused a cloud of dust to fill the room. When the cloud settled, the baker still couldn't see the mouse. Where had the little beast hidden himself? But since there was now a long line of customers, he went back to the shop. Angrily he looked at the squashed cake. He still had cream sticking to his face and now he was covered in flour. All the customers started to laugh at him, and in the end he had to laugh too. He cleared away the destroyed cake and tidied the shop until it was as clean as before. But, unseen by everyone, the little mouse crept back in under the counter where there were more cakes. With all the excitement, the mouse had got hungry again, and began to lick greedily at a thick chocolate cake.

Then Catherine and her mother came in. "Tomorrow it's my birthday," said Catherine, "and mummy's buying me a cake. Have you got any chocolate ones?" The baker reached under the counter and pulled out the chocolate cake, in which sat – the little mouse! The next day, Catherine's mother decorated the cake with seven candles. Now the mouse wasn't stupid and he knew he'd better take this opportunity to escape. Knowing he had spoiled the cake, he took some flowers from the vase and presented them to Catherine when she came in with her mother, so as to make up for it. Her mother was horrified, for no one could eat the cake now, but Catherine was delighted with the little mouse and wanted to play with him. The mouse however sprang quickly out of the open window, leaving the disappointed little girl behind. When her party guests arrived, she told them all about it.

18th August

The Little Town

In the night, musicians come,
While all the town's asleep,
They sing to strings of violins
While the penny whistle peeps.
The good old moon shines down on them,
And they play their tunes so loud,
He never says a single word,
But sweeps on through his clouds.

19th August

A Farmhouse says "Goodnight"

Before the sun disappears behind the mountains she says goodnight to the farmhouse in the little village, just as the cock says goodnight to his hens before hopping onto his perch and putting his head under his wing. He has to sleep because he has to wake the farmers at three o'clock to start the hay-harvest. But the hens still have so much to talk about and they gobble on until the cock comes to complain. How stupid his hens are! They've just got a lot of nonsense in their heads. He has to round them up and send them to bed, and then gradually everything goes quiet. Then from under the stairs comes a polecat who looks around with flashing eyes for the eggs that the farmer's wife has perhaps left behind. But it's still too bright for her, so she slinks back to her hiding-place. In the stable, Lisa the cow is licking her calf's dappled hide. Then she says *"Moo!"* which means goodnight. She's also saying goodnight to the tired oxen family and the Curlytail pig family, but they've been snoring away for a long time. They always forget to say goodnight and don't pay any attention to custom. That always annoys Lisa the cow.

20th August

The Pretty Little House (1)

On the meadow all alone,
There stands a house that's not a home,
Empty the cellar and empty the rooms,
The birds fly past its lonely gloom.
But one day Mrs. Grey the mouse,
Moves into the the sad dark house.

In the comfy cellar she makes her home,
And the house doesn't feel so much alone.
Then comes yellow Tiger kitten,
And finds the house is very fitting.
He curls up by the fireplace,
With a happy smile upon his face.

So now in the pretty little house,
Live Tiger Cat and Mrs. Grey Mouse.
Then the lively Family Swallow,
Are soon the cat and mouse to follow,

Of all the roofs this must be best,
To build their safe and roomy nest.
The swallows the cat and the little
mouse,
Have livened up the little house.
Then one day outside the house.

Of the cat, the swallows, and little mouse,
Along come a woman and a man,
With their baby and a furniture van.
Now the pretty house gently smiles,
For she is   the home of a little child.

The Pretty Little House (2)

The little house gets a garden,
The flowers bring much joy,
And charging on his scooter,
Comes the happy blonde-haired boy.
The baby, swallows, cat and mouse,
The blonde-haired boy all love the house.

Then comes Mr. Bailey,
With his wagging, barking friend,
And chasing balls in the garden,
His freedom has no end.
There's animals, people and a mouse,
And now a dog in the pretty house.

The pretty house is happy,
No more will she be blue,
The animals, birds and people,
Have made her dreams come true.
On the meadow not alone,
There stands a house that is a home.

At the next window now we see,
A small green chirping bird,
And such a lovely melody,
The house has never heard.
The last one is a little girl,
Her name is Anna-Lee,

She wears a rosy frilly dress,
And is as pretty as can be.
The pretty house is happy,
No more will she be blue,

22nd August

Out into the Country

What a surprise it would be if a car
suddenly pulled up outside your house
and asked you to go for a drive in the
country. I think you would be delighted
We were when Uncle Robert came by in
his new car with all our cousins, and our
parents let us go with him. We didn'
even say goodbye because we were so
excited. Uncle Robert drove and cousin
Frank sat beside him. We were only

interested in the car itself and not where we were driving, for Frank was showing us all the different parts of the car and what they were used for. So the time passed and we had no idea how far we'd gone. Then Uncle Robert stopped and we found ourselves before the farmhouse of a quaint little village. "Everyone out!" called Frank, and so we all sprang out. We didn't get to see much of the farm, for when we arrived, all the farmers were just going out onto the meadow for the hay harvest. As town children we were just as interested in the hay waggon as the new car, and when the farmer asked us if we'd like to have a ride, we didn't refuse! It was a very bumpy ride, but that didn't matter to us. And then the big scented meadow with all that hay was a real pleasure to see. We had a great time jumping somersaults and hiding among the hay bales.

We were covered in so much hay you could hardly recognise us. The farmers loaded the bales onto the waggons to take them back to the farm. We wanted to help, but unfortunately the waggon was already loaded so high we couldn't reach. We were however allowed to ride on top, but cousin Mary was too scared because it was so high and so she had to walk. When we got back to the farm we ate milk and thick slices of bread and butter. On the way back we asked Uncle Robert to take us out again some time!

23rd August

Rennie the Fox

In the wood in the dark hollow of a tree lives Mr. Fox and his wife with their three sons, Paul, Henry and the cheeky little Rennie. Mr. and Mrs. Fox aren't there today, they've gone into the village to fetch a hen. Rennie is bored, because his two lazy brothers are asleep and snoring, so he creeps out of the hollow into the morning light. This looks like fun! Little deers grazing at the forest edge and rabbits hopping over the grass. Naughty Rennie starts chasing the poor animals all over the forest. Whenever they hide, under stones or among the undergrowth he always finds them. Leave them alone, Rennie! The little rabbits run to the pond but Rennie runs after them.

But the rabbits are more nimble than he is, and they manage to avoid the water, but Rennie cannot put on his brakes in time and he falls – *splash!* – into the water. The ducks, flapping their wings in surprise, make him wetter and wetter, and soon he is covered in slime, And then on top of all that he finds himself being pelted with hazelnuts by the squirrel – how the rabbits laugh! With stiff and filthy limbs, Rennie goes back to the tree where his brothers are still snoring – perhaps it would have been better if he'd stayed asleep!

24th August

The Sleeping Beauty (1)

There was once a King and Queen who longed for a child, and eventually, the Queen had a little girl. She was so beautiful that the King wanted everyone to see her, and he threw a big party. He invited not only friends and relations, but also the wise fairies that lived in his Kingdom. But since he only had twelve golden plates, he decided not to invite the thirteenth fairy. When the celebration was over, the fairies gathered around the child's cradle, and each gave her a special gift. They wished her virtue, beauty, wealth and all the best things in the world. Just as the twelfth was about to give her wish, the thirteenth fairy stormed in. She was furious that she had not been invited, and she cursed the child in an angry voice, "On her fifteenth birthday, this child shall prick her fringer on a sprinning-wheel and die!" And then she flew out of the room. Everyone was

horrified, but the twelfth fairy went to the cradle and said, "I cannot reverse the curse, but I can soften it. She shall not die from the prick but shall fall into a deep sleep for a hundred years and only a prince can wake her!" Even so, the King burned every spinning wheel in the land.

25th August

The Sleeping Beauty (2)

The girl grew to fulfil all the wishes the good fairies had given her, and everyone loved her. Then, on her fifteenth birthday, she was wandering around the castle on her own. She came to an old tower. She climbed up the winding staircase and came to a door. She turned the rusty key, and when she went in she saw an ancient woman sitting at a spinning wheel. "Good day, madam," said the Princess, "what are you doing?" "I'm spinning," said the old lady. "What's that thing that's spinning around?" said the Princess. But scarcely had she touched the spindle, when she pricked herself, and she fell into a deep sleep. But not only did the Princess fall asleep, but the King, the Queen and the whole of the Court.
The horses slept in the stable, the dog in the yard and even the flies on the wall. The roast stopped cooking, and the cook fell asleep in the process of giving the serving boy a box on the ears. The wind stopped and all around the castle, a hedge of thorns started to grow up, which got higher and thicker every year, until the castle could no longer be seen.

The Sleeping Beauty (3)

The legend of the Sleeping Beauty grew, for this is what they called her. Princes from many lands tried to get through the thick thorn hedge to reach her, but every brave man died on the cruel spikes. Many many years later, another Prince came, and although he had heard how so many Princes before him had perished in the thorns, he was not afraid. By now a hundred years had passed, and as he was hacking away at the thorns with his sword, the thorns opened up of their own accord. He rushed on through the castle yard where the guards and the animals were sleeping and into the house where the flies were snoozing on the wall, and the cook was still poised to strike the boy. Finally he came to the tower, and he opened the door of the room where Sleeping Beauty had slept for a hundred years. When he saw her, struck by her beauty he just had to kiss her.

Scarcely had he done that when she opened her eyes and looked at him, and as they walked through the castle hand in hand, the whole court began to wake up. The horses neighed, the dogs jumped and the fire burned again, while the cook finally succeeded in boxing the boy's ears. The Prince went to Sleeping Beauty's mother and father and asked for her hand in marriage. The King delighted, and after the most wonderful wedding was celebrated, they lived happily from that day to this.

Peter Can Walk Today!

"Peter can walk!" someone shouts,
The echo flies away,
And reaches all the munching goats,
"Peter can walk today!"

"Peter can walk," hears the rubbish dump,
"Listen while I say!"
The bunnies' bobtails gladly thump,
Cos Peter can walk today!

Boldi Goes Back (1)

Tom was lying in a hammock reading an exciting story. Boldi sat nearby looking sadly into the bright daylight. When Tom noticed, he laid down his book and took Boldi in his arms. Then the little fellow started to sob. "Boldi, my little friend, what's wrong?" said Tom shocked. "Dear Tom," sobbed Boldi, "Please don't be angry with me! I feel so homesick for the wood, I've just got to go back there!" Tom thought for a while and then he said, "Do you know what! Next weekend we'll go to the wood where my dad has built a log cabin. Maybe that's the wood where you were born!" As soon as Boldi heard

this, he beamed such a bright smile that you'd never think he'd been sad. Sunday brought the sunshine, and Tom took his bike, put Boldi in the basket, and set off for the river where they got on the steamer to cross to the wood. The wind blew softly over the water, and they both felt so happy. When they reached the other bank, they got back on the bike and rode off. Soon they could smell mushrooms and strawberries. Then they came to the log cabin, and Boldi ran straight inside to investigate everything. This was something quite new for him. Then Tom put him on his lap and asked him if he felt better.

By the look of joy on his face, Boldi didn't even have to answer.

29th August

Boldi Goes Back (2)

Tom and Boldi soon made themselves comfortable in the cabin, and by evening Tom's parents were there too. Tom's mother lit a fire and soon it was really warm inside. The flames sparkled, and it gradually got dark. Suddenly they saw a pair of big glowing eyes outside the window, and Tom was terrified until his father explained that it was only Mr. Owl. Tom became very relieved, but Boldi was extremely excited, for he was certain that he knew the owl, so he waited until everyone was asleep, and crept out into the wood. When the owl saw him, he looked, then he looked again, and said, "Aren't you Boldi, the one who went among the humans over a year ago?" "Yes! And you're the owl that persuaded my parents to let me go!" beamed Boldi with happiness, for now he was sure that this was the wood where he had grown up, and he just couldn't wait to see all his old friends again. With this thought his heart almost burst with joy, he'd been away for so long! But the owl interrupted his thoughts. "My dear Boldi, I find it excellent that you have kept your promise to return, and tomorrow we animals will throw a huge celebration in your honour!"

"That's wonderful, Mr. Owl," said Boldi, "But I can bring Tom too, can't I? "And who is Tom? asked the owl, and so Boldi told him the whole story. The owl listened attentively and then he said, "Yes, of course Tom can come. He can tell us about the humans. All the animals will be thrilled." The next morning, Boldi woke Tom and told him everything. The boy was delighted and couldn't wait for the party.

Boldi Goes Back (3)

The day passed far too slowly, but in the end they went out into the wood. All the animals were there, for none of them were afraid of Tom since the owl had told them all about him. It was really wonderful! At last Boldi got to see his hedgehog parents and his brothers and sisters, but it was even better to see the daughter of the hedgehogs from next door! Boldi danced with her all night, and when the time came to go, he just couldn't leave her, he didn't know why. Then he realised that he must love the little hedgehog! So he told Tom and his parents, and they decided to ask the owl. The owl put his head on one side and thought for a long time. Then he said, "You'll have to get married, that's the only solution! I myself will marry you."
Then he added, "I know that Tom's father has a log cabin, and if Boldi and his wife were allowed to live there, then Tom could visit him every weekend and wouldn't have to say goodbye forever!"
Tom was so glad when he heard that! How wise the owl was! So next Sunday, Boldi was to be married!

Boldi Goes Back (4)

Tom wanted to surprise Boldi and his wife, so he went back to his parents and told them what had happened and what his plan was. His mother laughed when she heard what her son was going to do, and dad set about helping him straight away. Tom was given tools and wood, and after school every day he was allowed to go to the wood. In the cabin he set to work with his carpentry, and after a lot of shaving and sticking, he had built a proper little flat for the couple, with rooms and staircases! Another surprise would be the entrance he had built into the log cabin! Tom had worked so hard that it was all ready by Sunday. When the couple saw it, they were so pleased! Tom often came to visit them, and there were always new things to talk about, especially since now there were lots of little hedgehogs running about the house!
They all looked exactly like proper hedgehogs except for one thing – they all had little red spikes on their heads, just like Boldi's. Boldi was so proud!

1st September

The Dear Little Sunny Ray

The starlings criss-cross in the sky,
The storks have flown all day,
They're on the way to Africa,
And it's a long, long way!
September, though you chase away,
The birds in all their stress,
Please shine down on the apples,
And give them a new red dress!
Now sunny ray has a shorter stay,
And deep in clouds he hides away.

2nd September

Journey to the Sea

When father came and smilingly announced, "Tomorrow we're going to the seaside," we thought he was joking, but he really meant it! How exciting it was, especially while we were packing. But there still wasn't room to take everything we wanted to. "You don't need that!" said dad, "There's so many things to do at the seaside that you won't need all your old toys!" Since dad had already been to the seaside, we thought it must be true. That night none of us could sleep, and it wasn't until we were standing on the train platform that we calmed down, for now we were on our way. Dad had chosen windowseats in the train, and it was wonderful to see the meadows, dark forests and fields flashing past. Because it was travelling at an incredible speed, we soon reached our destination. We were glad to get out really, because the journey had made us very tired, and after a super supper, we all fell exhausted into bed. The next day we were to take the steamer to the Island, which was our final destination. who can describe our joy when we saw the wide sea with its ships stretching before us? There we sat in our boat, and after half an hour we came to the lovely white sands and sand dunes.

Then we discovered the harbour with all its proud ships. Everything was so new for us that we were quite overpowered. We came to the fine beach hotel, and we had only one wish – to stay here as long as possible! It was so good playing in the sand, that not for a minute did we think of our toys in the hotel room. We built mountains, holes, castles with moats; we gathered mussels, went fishing, built ships to our hearts' content. Of course we went swimming every day. In the evenings we walked along the prom or rode in the motor boat. Unfortunately the holiday was over only too quickly. But we knew we'd be coming back soon.

How Little Thomas Learned How to Get Up

sight. The baker dropped his rolls and the milkman spilt his milk. The clothes reached the school, and ran inside. Thomas looked desperately in through the window, and his friend Henry called, "What are you doing here in your pyjamas?" Thomas was so ashamed and began to cry, and these tears woke him up, for he was only sleeping, thank goodness! There stand his clothes, waiting for him. Now mother has no trouble getting him up in the morning, and as soon as the cuckoo calls, Thomas is completely ready for school!

Thomas is a very nice little boy, but he just can't get up in the mornings! The sun looks in and tickles him on his nose, the cuckoo chirps out the time from his clock, but the boy takes no notice and just pulls the covers up around him. Then one day, one of Thomas's shoes said, "I'm tired of being late for school every day! I say we should go without him!" The socks cried "Hurray!" and soon all his clothes began to gather, his trousers, his shirt and his cap, and they cried, "Let's go!" This cry woke Thomas, and when he saw his clothes disappearing out of the door, he jumped out of bed as though something had bitten him! But they didn't wait for him, and he had to chase them all through the streets. All the other boys and girls giggled at him, and people opened their windows and laughed at the

On the Sheep's Meadow

In the middle of the meadow lies the old sheepstall. White-blooming elder bushes look curiously over its roof, and nothing in the whole land blooms as beautifully as here. The sheep hop here and there over the meadow, and choose a leaf here, a flower there, for on this meadow they can afford to be choosey. *"Bah, Bah,"* go the two little lambs Bimmel and Bammel, as they gamble all around making their little bells ring. Bimmel has a red ribbon around her neck, for she's a lady.

But Bammel proudly wears a blue ribbon, for he's going to be a ram. The bell is particularly important for Bammel, for he can use it to chase away the crows and sparrows that want to bathe in his

water-trough. Also, whenever a sheep wanders from the meadow, the bell always leads the farmer to where he is. But today by the sheep-stall, Bammel has made a new discovery – how can there be an animal smaller than a lamb, but with ears bigger than a sheep? Crisscross the little rabbit is also a runaway. He was so bored in his hutch that he gnawed a hole in the side and ran away. Who knows where Crisscross will go next?

5th September

The World Upside Down

In the evenings when I get up,
After mornings in my bed,
The hens they crow and the cock it cackles,
And the world stands on its head.
The maid puts the oven in the fire,
The wife puts the soup in peas,
The servant sweeps the broom with the room,
While the books the children read!
It hurts to put my boots in my feet,
And on my hat my head,
And it's not so comfy when I sleep,
At the bottom of my bed!

6th September

A Farmhouse says "Goodnight"

Behind the stove in the farmhouse, the cat stretches from his sleep, for work is just beginning for him. As he licks himself, he wonders how he can catch the mouse family who have just moved into the granary. So he impatiently waits for little Frank to let him go as he hugs him before he goes to bed. Then the farmer's wife takes him and lays him in his soft bed where she tells him about the little sand-men. From the veranda, the geraniums wave goodnight to their flower-sisters in the garden. They all whisper back goodnight, and don't even forget the cabbages, who were very grumpy today and didn't join in the conversation at all. When the evening wind waved through the garden, they only nodded their heads in greeting, so as not to wake the midgets and butterflies, who were already dreaming among their leaves. A hedgehog peeps out of his hole and waits until everything's quiet before he goes for his walk. A toad snaps up a beetle, who has been to a meadow party and who had lingered too long. The water in the fountain now settles down, and the moon points its silvery finger at the farmer and his wife who are sitting outside on a bench. They're happy to relax for a while after the day's hard work.

When at last they go in and close the door, Rover the dog barks his goodnight greeting, and starts off on his first tour. He stays awake to make sure that none of the sleepers are disturbed.

7th September

Heidi in the Alps (1)

On a bright sunny morning in June, a young woman was walking up a narrow mountain path holding a little girl by the hand. When they were halfway up they met Peter with his herd of goats, who was also going up the mountain. Heidi, as the little girl was called, liked the goats very much, and so she climbed up behind

them. Her heavy clothes and the heat made this very difficult, so she sat down and took off her shoes and socks and all her other clothes until she was only wearing her underclothes. Then she laid all her clothes on a stone and climbed up beside Peter and the goats as nimbly as can be. When her aunt saw Heidi there in her underclothes, she cried out, "Heidi! Where have you put all your new clothes?" Heidi calmly pointed down the mountain. "You are naughty!" she called, "How are we going to fetch them back? Come on, Peter! Go and fetch them!" So Peter ran like the wind down the mountain and brought the clothes back.

Meanwhile, Heidi had run on and had already reached the top. There sat grandad on a bench smoking his pipe. Heidi went up to him, put out her hand and said, "Good day, grandfather!" Then Aunty arrived with Peter. "Good day!" she said, "I've brought you the child from

160

your son Tobias. I've been looking after her since Tobias and his wife died. Now it's up to you to do your share!" "And what am I supposed to do?" said the old man. "That's your problem," said Aunty, "I've got a job in Frankfurt and I can't take the child with me!" Grandfather looked at her angrily, and Aunty ran down the mountain feeling very guilty, for the old man was known in all the village as a disobliging and bad-tempered man.

8th September

Heidi in the Alps (2)

Heidi loved it at her grandfather's, specially because of the food which tasted so nice up here in the fresh air. "Where shall I sleep, grandad?" asked Heidi. "Where you want!" was the reply.

That was fine by Heidi, and she ran all over the house until she climbed a ladder and found herself in the hay loft. "I'll sleep here!" she called down, "It's lovely up here!" And with grandad's help she had soon made a comfy bed out of hay and a few sheets.

"I wish it was already night-time and I could go to bed!" said Heidi. But it wasn't time for bed yet, so Heid went behind the house to the big old fir trees. There the wind was so strong that it whistled eerily all around. Then there came a shrill whistle, and goat after goat sprang up beside her, followed by Peter in the middle. They all stood still at the house, and Heidi stroked two fine goats that came towards her. "Go and get a bowl and some bread," said grandad. Grandad milked a goat, gave the bowl and the bread to Heidi and said, "Now eat that and go to bed," then he disappeared into the stable. Heidi did as she was told, then she climbed into her new bed and slept happily and deeply all night. Next morning Heidi was woken by another loud whistle, and she sprang out of bed and got dressed. Out in the yard was Peter with his herd. "Do you want to go with him onto the pasture?" asked grandad. Heidi, of course, jumped around in delight. "But go and get washed first!" Meanwhile grandad packed lots of food for them and warned Peter to take good care of Heidi. It was wonderful out there on the mountain

come anymore. Eventually it stopped and grandad was able to go out and clear the snow away a little bit. Soon there was a knock at the door and in came Peter covered in snow. He stood in front of the fire to thaw himself out, and meanwhile grandad prepared a fine supper. After Peter had eaten as much as he could, he got ready to go, but before he went, he said "I'm coming again on Sunday, and you must come with me to visit my gran." That was something completely different for Heidi, to go and visit someone, and she wouldn't give her grandad any peace until he agreed to take her. So one day he covered her up warmly and took her with a sledge to Peter's cottage. There she met Peter's blind grandmother.

She couldn't understand why Heidi's hands were so warm when she had been out in the cold.

"Oh, I wasn't cold at all!" said Heidi. "Grandad wrapped me up in a very, very thick blanket."

Peter's mother was very surprised and

with Peter, but what was most beautiful of all was the Alpine sunset in the evening. Heidi sat quite still and couldn't stop looking at it.

From then on, Heidi always went with Peter, until Autumn came and the weather got colder. "Now you'll have to stay at home, Heidi," said grandad, "A little girl like you would be blown over the cliff when the wind hits you!" Peter didn't like that at all, for without Heidi it would be so boring.

9th September

Heidi in the Alps (3)

But one night the snow came, and by morning the whole mountain was covered. Because of this, Peter couldn't

aid, "The child probably doesn't know that her grandad hasn't been out among people for years and years."

But then they heard loud banging from outside. "That's grandad!" cried Heidi, "He brought his hammer and nails with him to clear the snow off your house. Peter had told him how bad it was."

Yes, Olaf, Heidi's grandad, had changed. Now his life had some meaning again, because now he had Heidi who loved him so much, and who thought life in the Alps was the best life in the world.

10th September

Heidi Leaves (1)

Heidi had now lived with her grandad for a long time, and she was so happy there. She was now eight years old, and she had learned so many things from Olaf. She was very good with the goats, and two in particular followed her around like faithful dogs, and bounded towards her whenever they heard her voice. One day just after lunch, a visitor came. It was Aunty Deta. She was beautifully dressed, and had on a lovely hat with a feather in

it. Olaf looked her up and down, but didn't say a word.

But Deta was determined to be friendly to Olaf, for she wanted to take Heidi with her to Frankfurt. She told him she had always

intended to take Heidi back, and that was why she had come. Heidi now had the chance in a thousand, to live with the very rich relations of her boss, who had an only child who had to spend the rest of her life in a wheelchair. Because of this she was often alone and would dearly love a playmate. Her mother had asked for a completely unspoiled child, and

Deta had thought of Heidi. "Have you finished?" interrupted Olaf, "Heidi and I don't want to know!" "If that's how you feel then I'll put it to you differently!" said Deta, "This child is now eight years old. If you refuse to let her go to school and to Church you are breaking the law. Do you want to go to court?" "Shut up!" thundered Olaf, "Take her and spoil her then, and don't ever let me set eyes on you again!" Then Olaf stormed out of the room. "You've made grandad angry," said Heidi. "He'll get over it," answered Deta, "Come on!" "I'm not coming!" said Heidi. "Don't be silly!" snapped Deta, "You've no idea how lovely it is in Frankfurt, and if you don't like it, then you can come back. By then grandad will feel better."

In the end, Heidi let herself be persuaded, and she went off down the mountain with her Aunt. On the way she met Peter. "Where are you going?" he asked astonished. "I've got to go to Frankfurt with Aunty," Heidi said, but Deta pulled her on, so she couldn't say any more. Peter rushed into the cottage and told his grandmother that Heidi was going to Frankfurt. His gran stumbled to the window, tore open the window and cried out, "Deta! Don't take the child away from us!" Heidi wanted to turn back and run to them, but Deta stopped her and said, "You can come back straight away and bring back something nice for gran!" This was such a lovely thought that she began to rush on ahead, even through the village, so that everyone thought she couldn't wait to get away from Olaf. Poor old Olaf became as bad-tempered as he had been before.

Heidi Leaves (2)

Meanwhile, Deta and Heidi had reached Frankfurt, and they were standing in front of the house where Heidi was to stay. Deta asked the carriage driver if it was alright to see Miss Rottenmyer now. "That's not my concern," said the driver, "You'll have to ring the bell."

Deta rang the bell and the butler came. "That's not my concern," said the butler, "Ring Miss Tinnet." And he disappeared. Miss Tinnet was sent for, and when she came she said, "You are expected." They were taken into the study where Miss Rottenmyer was waiting. "What's your name?" she asked Heidi. "Heidi," said Heidi clearly. "Heidi! That's no Christian name! And how old is the child? She doesn't look twelve to me!" "She'll soon be ten," said Deta hopefully. "I'm eight grandad said," explained Heidi. Miss Rottenmyer was not pleased. "And what have you studied?" "Nothing," answered Heidi truthfully. "Miss Deta," said Miss Rottenmyer, "this is completely out of order! How could you have brought me this child?" But Deta was not to be put off, and she defended herself until in the end she said, "And I've got to go now in any case, my boss is waiting for me." And after curtseying she went out of the door and downstairs. Heidi was left alone. Clara waved at her from her wheelchair, and the children had already made friends. Clara liked Heidi very much.

Heidi Leaves (3)

Miss Rottenmyer was quite agitated because Clara's playmate was not at all as she had expected. In the dining room she discovered Sebastian, the butler. Miss Rottenmyer called Miss Tinnet and told her to make sure the new arrival's room was ready. When Sebastian had cast a proud eye over his table to make sure everything was there, he went into the study to fetch Clara in her wheelchair. Heidi sat down near to where Sebastian was serving and said, "You look like Peter!" Miss Rottenmyer clapped her hands in horror. "Is it possible! Now she's hobnobbing with the servants! The child has no upbringing!" Heidi was as quiet as a mouse at the table after that, she didn't move. The resemblance she had found between Sebastian and Peter

must have made her trust him, and when he came to serve the meat, she pointed to the bread on her plate and said, "Can I have that?" She wanted to take it to gran. Sebastian nodded, so she took it and put it in her pocket. Then when he came and stood before her with a silver plate, he looked at her silently for a while. "Am I to help myself? asked Heidi in the end. Sebastian nodded, for he was not

allowed to speak at the dinner table. But when Heidi tried to help herself, Sebastian wanted to laugh, and he nearly dropped the plate. "You can leave the plate on the table and come back later," said Miss Rottenmyer sternly. Sebastian disappeared. "Well, Heidi," she said, "I can see I shall have to teach you how to serve yourself at table!"

And then she explained clearly what Heidi had to do. "And then I'll have to make sure that you don't speak to

Sebastian at the table," and so she went on, and on, with all sorts of rules and regulations, until Heidi simply fell asleep, for she had been up since five, and had had a very long journey. When in the end Miss Rottenmyer said, "Now Heidi, think about it!" Clara had to laugh. "Heidi's been asleep a long time!" Supper hadn't been so amusing for a long time!

13th September

Old Sultan

A farmer once had a very faithful dog who was very old. The farmer said to his wife, "I think I should shoot Sultan, because he's no use to us anymore." "But he's served us for so long!" said his wife. But the farmer stood by his decision. Now the dog had heard everything, and he was heartbroken. That evening he went to his friend the wolf and told him. "Don't worry," said the wolf, 'I'll tell you what to do. Tomorrow morning the farmer and his wife will go to the hay harvest. They'll take their child with them and put him by the hedge. You lay beside him as though you're looking after him. Then I'll come

and try to take the child away. You chase me, and they'll think you saved the child! That way they'll keep you forever!"
The dog thought this was a good idea, and they carried it out as they had planned. The wolf snatched the child, Sultan chased him, and carried the child back to its parents. They were so overjoyed that they gave the dog everything, and he's never had it so good. Then the wolf visited the dog and said, "I'm sure now you won't object if I take one of your master's sheep!" But Sultan remained faithful to his master, and told him what the wolf had in mind.

The farmer lay in wait, and when the wolf came he thrashed him mercilessly. Furious, the wolf demanded a duel with the dog. The wolf was first on the spot, and accompanying him was a wild boar, but all the dog had was a lame cat. But when the wolf and the boar saw Sultan and the cat limping along, they thought the cat was picking up stones as he stooped down, and because they were afraid, they made peace!

14th September

The Horse with no Rear-end

Once during a war, we drove the Turks

into their town and then straight out again. With my fiery steed, I was at the front. Suddenly I was standing alone in the market place, and while my horse was drinking out of the fountain, I looked around me. But what was that!
My horse was missing its rear-end, and the water that it was drinking came splashing out behind him onto the street. A servant explained the puzzle: just as I was storming through the town gate, the gate came crashing down from above and chopped off the horse's rear-end! Our blacksmith fused the two parts together and before long the miracle-horse was back to normal again.

15th September

The Corn-ears

A long time ago, when God Himself still walked the Earth, the fertility of the land was much greater than now. The corn-ears were just as long as the stem. But Mankind never looks after the things that God gives them, and they always take them for granted. One day, a woman was walking past a cornfield with her little child, and the child fell into a puddle and dirtied her clothes. Her mother tore off a handful of the corn-ears and cleaned the dress with them. When God saw this, he was angry and said, "From now on, there will be no more ears of corn. Mankind is no longer worthy of Heavenly gifts." Those standing around fell on their knees in fear, and begged God to leave the ears. The innocent hens who didn't deserve it, would starve without the ears. The Lord relented, but gave corn the small ears that they have now.

16th September

Ring-a-ring o'Roses

Ring-a-ring o' roses,
A pocket full of posies,
Atishoo! Atishoo!
We all fall down.

Bill the Clown (1)

Bill the Clown was a rascal from the day he was born. Once his mother took him to the fair, and Bill drank until he was dizzy. Then, towards evening, he got tired and crawled into an empty bee-hive to sleep for a while. Now, in the night, along came two thieves who wanted to steal some honey, and they picked up each basket in turn to see which was the heaviest. Bill woke up and heard the thieves talking about their theft. Because it was so dark and impossible to see, Bill put his arm out of the hive and pulled one of the thief's hair. The man got angry and shouted at the other thief, because he thought it was him. "How could I have pulled your hair?" the second one cried, "I can hardly carry the basket with my hands." Then Bill pulled the other thief's hair so hard that he screached. "First you say I pulled your hair, and now you're pulling mine! Just wait till I get my hands on you!" And a great battle began.

They dropped the bee-hive on the floor and punched each other all down the street until they disappeared. Then Bill simply climbed out of the basket and went home!

18th September

Bill the Clown (2)

When Bill was older, he told everyone that he was going to walk a tight-rope across the street, so he attached a rope from his house to the house opposite, and a crowd of spectators gathered below to watch him break his neck! But before he started he demanded that every spectator should give him their left shoe, and everyone was only too

Bill the Clown (3)

Once Bill became a servant in the house of a priest, but the priest didn't know what a rascal he had just employed. The priest said to him, "You'll be very happy here, I think. You shall eat and drink just as well as my cook and me, and you can take your time over everything you have to do." That sounded alright! Now the Priest had a cook who only had one eye. She had prepared two chickens and had put them on the spit, and she told Bill to turn it. This he did, and when the chickens were done, he said to himself, "The Priest said I should eat as well as him and the cook, so I'll make sure he keeps his word!" and he took one of the chickens and ate it! When it was nearly suppertime, the one-eyed cook came back and she could only see one chicken. "Where's the other one?" she asked. "Open up your other eye and you will see it," answered Bill cheekily. The cook angrily ran to the Priest and told him everything. The Priest went to Bill and said, "Where is the other chicken?" "There's the other chicken on the spit," replied Bill.

The Priest laughed, "And so where is the first one?" "I've eaten the first one," replied Bill, "because you said I was to eat as well as you and the cook, and if you'd eaten both chickens that would have made you a liar, and I wanted to avoid that!" The Priest laughed again, and said that from now on he was to do as he was told by the cook. Now when the cook gave him work to do, he only did half of it. When the cook complained to the Priest, Bill said the cook could only see half of everything, and so he only did half the work. That made the Priest laugh again. But the Cook said that if Bill stayed, she would go, so the Priest was forced, against his will, to let Bill go.

pleased, for they wondered what he was going to do with them. He attached them all to a piece of string and climbed up onto the rope with them. Everyone waited expectantly. Then Bill cried, "Ladies and gentlemen! Look for your shoes!" Then he cut off the knot from the string and the shoes went hurtling down into the street. The crowd rushed madly at the shoes trying to find which one was theirs. One cried "That's my shoe!" While the other cried, "You liar, it's mine!" So they began to tear each other's hair out and fight like dogs; even the old people were slapping each other. But Bill the Clown just sat on his rope and laughed. When he got fed up, he just got down and left the others fighting for shoes. After this, Bill couldn't go out onto the street for four weeks. He had to stay in the house patching shoes.

20th September

Bill the Clown (4)

A rich business-man was going into his garden when he saw Bill lying on a meadow. The man asked him what he was doing, and Bill answered that he was a cook who was out of work. "I'll give you a job and pay you well for it," said the business man. "My wife will thank me, because she hates cooking!" Bill promised to work well.

The next day, Bill was supposed to do a roast. The business man said to him, "Cook the roast slowly and baste it well so that it doesn't burn, then try to keep it cool." So Bill put the meat on a spit between two barrels of wine in the cellar, which was the coolest place he could find, and of course the barrels caught fire! When the business man asked him what had happened, he had to laugh at Bill's stupidity, but his wife didn't laugh! Next the business man took Bill with him on a journey to pacify his wife. Before they drove into town, the business man said to Bill, "Now be careful of the path you take, and don't look around." As they were going along a very stoney path, the back of the cart came off, but of course Bill didn't look around and carried on driving on his own. The business man called after him, but Bill didn't hear, so the man had to walk the rest of the way, and by the time he got there, his tongue was hanging out nearly down to his neck! After they had finished their business, they drove home, but the business man didn't want to keep Bill anymore, and he said to him, "Tonight you can stay, but tomorrow you can clear out of the house, because you're nothing but a rogue!"

So the next morning, when the man had left, Bill began to clear the house out! He dragged every piece of furniture he could carry out onto the street, while all the neighbours wondered what on earth was happening. Someone went and told the business, man and he rushed back in a great state of agitation! "What are you doing, you wretch!" shouted the man. "I'm clearing out the house, as you told me to," explained Bill. And then he walked away, leaving the poor business man to drag everything back in. He was furious, but the neighbours laughed about it for a long time to come!

Bill the Clown (5)

Bill played his tricks all over the land, until the people complained about him to the Duke, and the Duke banished him. But Bill took no notice and carried on riding through. He had just bought a horse and cart filled with earth from a farmer he had worked for a while. One day the Duke rode towards him, and Bill sprang down from his horse and jumped into the cart filled with earth. The Duke rode up to him and said, ''Get out of my land, don't you know I've banished you and that if I find you, you're to be hung?''

But Bill answered, ''I haven't done anything that you can hang me for, Your Majesty!''
''What do you mean by that?'' asked the Duke. ''I'm sitting on my own land that I have bought and paid for,'' replied Bill. Now there was nothing the Duke could do, so he rode off angrily.

22nd September

Bill the Clown (6)

One day a barber employed Bill. He said to him, ''Do you see that house over there with the big windows? Go in and I'll be along in a minute.'' So Bill went to the house and climbed in through the big

windows! The barber's wife was sitting in the room and screamed in terror, "Are you from the devil?" Bill replied, "If that's what your husband's called, yes! I'm the new employee." Meanwhile the barber came back and said, "Why couldn't you you go in through the door?" "Dear master, you told me to come in where the big windows were," replied Bill. The barber had to bite his tongue, for he needed Bill and hoped to get a tax reduction through paying his wages. After a few days of working at the barber's, Bill had to sharpen the scissor blades, but he did it in such a way that the back of the scissors were as sharp as the blade. The barber was furious, and he said to Bill, "Stop sharpening and go back to where you came!" So Bill went back to the big windows and sprang out the same way he had come in!

23rd September

Bill the Clown (7)

When Bill came to Oxford, he put a notice on the door of the big famous University. The Professors had heard all about him, and didn't want to be tricked like everyone else. The notice said that Bill could teach anyone to read and write in a very short time, so the Professors said to him, "You say you can teach anyone to read and write. Do you think you can teach this donkey?" Bill said, "Yes, of course! But you'll have to give me plenty of time, because he's a very stupid creature." So they gave him twenty years. So Bill took the donkey to an inn, and got a stable to teach him in. He took an old book and laid it on the cart. Between every page he put an ear of corn. The donkey turned the pages with his mouth and ate the corn, and when the corn ran out, he said "EA, EA!" When he had got the donkey to do that, he went to the Dean and said to him, "When do you want to see how far the donkey has got?" The Dean said, "If your pupil has learned anything at all, I'd like to see it straight away!" The donkey hadn't eaten anything all day, and when Bill came, he put a new book before him with corn in between the leaves, so the donkey turned the leaves and ate the corn. As soon as the corn ran out, he went, "EA, EA." Bill said, "You see, Dean, he can already say the two vowels I and A. I'm sure he will be very clever."

Bill the Clown (8)

When Bill got old and ill he made his will, and he divided his goods into three parts. The first part went to his friends, the second to the Counsellor, and the third to the Priest. But he stressed that he was to be given a Christian burial, and his treasure trunk was only to be opened four weeks after his death. Then he gave each of his benefactors a key, so that they could open the chest together, and share whatever they found there. Soon afterwards, Bill died. Then the Counsellor, the Priest and Bill's friends came together to open the chest, but when they opened it, they found nothing but stones. Each one suspected the other of stealing the treasure. The Priest thought it was the Counsellor, the Counsellor thought it was Bill's friends, but the friends thought the Priest had taken it after Bill had been to Confession. Well, they argued and accused, until they all went away cursing, and this was the last trick that Bill the Clown ever played! He had thought about it long before he died.

He had imagined what would happen, and as you can see, he definitely had the last laugh! But this wasn't the only strange thing that happened after his death! When everyone was gathered around his coffin in the graveyard, the coffin-bearers laid the coffin on the two ropes above the grave to lower it in. Suddenly the ropes snapped and the coffin shot down so that Bill was left standing upright! The people standing around were all of the same opinion: 'We should let him remain standing, for he was an extraordinary man when he lived, and he would probably want to remain extraordinary in his death!'' So there he stayed, and on the grave was put a stone engraved with the words: HERE STANDS BILL THE CLOWN, BURIED IN THE YEAR 1350.

25th September

Felix and the Apple-juice

sleeps as deeply as the wolf with the seven goats in his belly before he fell into the stream. Then the farmer discovers the empty jug, and realises that Felix has got drunk on cider! He is laughed at by the whole farmyard, especially the other goat Ferdinand, who goes and tells his girlfriend the whole story about Felix and the cider!

26th September

Do You Know How Many Stars There Are?

Do you know how many stars
Twinkle in the sky?
Do you know how many clouds
Blow through the world and why?
God the Lord counts all,
And he helps if one should fall,
From His big wide flock,
From His big wide flock.

27th September

Jock the Cock and Mush the Mouse

Jock the Cock rules the roost in the hen stall, and his word goes on the farm. He's the only one who calls "Cocka doodledoo!" in the morning, and the

When Felix the goat moves around under the apple tree, he looks as though butter wouldn't melt in his mouth, he's so sweet! And the snow-white goose Felicity is surely an enchanted Princess, for she walks so daintily and her feathers shine like silk. But it just so happens that Felix and Felicity sometimes get tired of just looking pretty, and so they go out walking. Felicity snatches the farmer's wife best stockings from the line and chews them. Now they're ruined and the wife is very angry. Felix discovers a jug full of fresh apple juice, and he gulps the whole lot down. Suddenly the goat gets dizzy and can hardly stand up. Everyone is horrified and thinks he must be really ill. With glassy eyes he staggers around, and in the end he just collapses. Then he hens huddle together on the perch to sleep when he tells them to.

Only the chicken is allowed to sit on her soft nest, because she's taking care of six little golden chicks underneath her wings. When the farmer's wife comes in and scatters corn over the floor, all the hens scrabble around on the floor to get as much as they can. But what a treat it is when they sometimes manage to find a worm or a beetle! You should hear the chickens cheep then! But they're not the only animals who live in the stall; so does Mush the mouse. He doesn't get such nice food as his cousin Max who lives in the kitchen, but then he has more risks to take, for the cat never comes into the hen stall since the cock pecked him when he was trying to get a closer look at the new chicks! Even Mush is afraid of Jock when he comes strutting past so proudly. Then he'd rather hide, for you never know with him! But when he goes out into the garden and crows down from his high throne, Mush rushes out too and nibbles at a juicy turnip or a fresh radish.

King Thrushbeard (1)

A King once had a beautiful daughter. He wanted her to get married, but she was so obstinate and proud that she mocked every suitor that came to her.

So the King prepared a big Ball to which he invited every eligible man in his Kingdom. He stood them all in a line according to their rank. First came the Kings, then the Dukes, the Princes, the Barons and finally the noblemen. Then the Princess was led down the line, but she had a word of mockery for them all. She especially mocked a certain very good King who had an unfortunate crooked chin. The Princess giggled, "He's got a chin like a thrush's beak!" This made her father very angry, and he swore that she should marry the first man who came to the door. One day a minstrel came and sang under her window, so the King told him to come in and he made his daughter marry him. Then he said to his daughter, "You can't stay in the Castle now, go with your husband!" So the beggar-minstrel took his wife and soon they came to a big wood. The Princess asked who it belonged to, and the minstrel said it belonged to King Thrushbeard, for this is what he had come to be called. The Princess said, "Oh, woe is me! If only I had married King Thrushbeard!" Then they went through a meadow and a lovely town that also belonged to King Thrushbeard. In the end they stopped at a tiny little house.

The Princess asked who this wretched little house belonged to, and the minstrel replied, "This belongs to you and me!" Then she had to cook and afterwards she fell sadly into bed.

29th September

King Thrushbeard (2)

Every morning the Princess had to get up very early and work, until one day her husband said, "Wife, we can't go on earning no money anymore, you'll have to start weaving baskets," so he went out and cut reeds. But when she began to weave, the hard reeds cut into her fingers and made them bleed, so her husband told her she had better start spinning instead, but the thread soon cut her tender hands to ribbons. "You're no good for any work," said the man bitterly, "I'll have to start making saucepans and and you can go to market to sell them." At first everything went well, and everyone thronged around this beautiful lady to buy her wares. Some people gave the money without even taking the saucepans! But one day a drunken Knight rode right through her stall and smashed everything to pieces. Now she was afraid to go home, and when she finally did, her husband had left her. So she lived alone in near poverty until one day she was invited to a wedding at the Castle, and she took with her a bowl and a little bag. As she was filling the bowl with soup and the bag with bread to take home with her, a man took her by the arm, and she felt so ashamed! But it was

King Thrushbeard, and he said to her, "I was the beggar-man and the drunken Knight, and I did all this to teach you a lesson, which I know you've learned.

Now we can really be married!" And so they were married, and at the fine wedding, the Princess's father smiled at last!

30th September

Good day, Mr. Monday

Good day, Mr. Monday!
How's Mr. Tuesday?
Is Mr. Wednesday at home?
Tell Mr. Thursday,
That Mrs. Friday
On Saturday is coming to see Mother Sunday.

1st October

The Dear Little Sunny Ray

October's come and the sunny ray
Can rest a little time,
The children run into the fields
And fly their kites so high.
Although October wind is hard,
The children play and laugh,
For through their cosy winter clothes,
The wind can find no path.

2nd October

Henry Dumm

There was once a King who lived happily
with his only daughter. But one day the
Princess had a baby, and no one knew
who the father was. The King told the
Princess to go into the Church and give
the baby a lemon, and whoever the child
gave the lemon to must be its father and
the man the Princess should marry. Now
only handsome people were allowed into
the Church. But a little hunch-backed boy
slipped in between the crowd unseen,
and it was to this boy, who was called
Henry Dumm, that the baby gave the
lemon. The King was so dismayed that he
put the shocked Princess and Henry into
a barrel and cast them out onto the sea.
When they were alone, the Princess said
to Henry, "You horrid hunchbacked-boy,
this is all your fault. The child had nothing
to do with you!" "Oh yes it had!" said
Henry, "because I once wished that you
would have a child, and what I wish
comes true."

"If that's true, then wish us something to
eat!" snapped the Princess. "I can do
that," said Henry, and he wished a bowl
of potatoes, and because she was so
hungry the Princess ate them all. Henry
wished for a fine ship, and then they had
everything in abundance. The ship soon
reached the shore, and Henry then
wished for a castle. Scarcely had he
wished, when before them stood a
wonderful castle, and a servant led them
inside. When they were inside, Henry
said, "Now I'd like to be a clever,
handsome Prince!" and his hunchback
disappeared and he became a young

Prince and the Princess was only too pleased to marry him. For a long time they lived happily together, until one day the Princess's father lost his way and ended up at the castle. He was heartily welcomed, but he didn't recognise his daughter, for he thought she had been drowned long ago. As he was going, the Princess secretly hid a golden cup in his pocket, and as he was riding away, she sent some servants after him, pretending he had stolen it. When they found the cup on him they brought him back. He swore to the Princess that he had not stolen it. "So one must not be ready to accuse someone straight away!" said the Princess.

And she held out her daugther to him. The King was overjoyed, and he lived with them from then on. When he died, Henry Dumm became King.

3rd October

What Happens Behind the Pig-stall

Today the pig-stall is going to be thoroughly cleaned, and so the two funny little pigs Resa and Rosa are allowed to plod around outside for a while. Squeaking, they run around all over the yard, and run over everything that stands in their way. Buckets, and brooms and even the farmer's wife herself. When they have had enough of running around, they sniff in every corner to see if there's anything to eat. The best thing is rummaging in the manure heap. Pitter and Patter, the two rabbits, are also let out when the stall's being cleaned. At first they hide when the two pigs are charging through the yard, but now they carefully hop about looking for some turnips. There's one! But Rosa has already seen it, and grunts towards it. Who's going to get it? The pig and the rabbits slowly move in for the catch, but a loud cry sends them all rushing for cover – a hen has just laid an egg! And that's the end of the story!

4th October

Carnival

What's that I hear, what's that I see?
People laughing, running, singing,
Oh mother, what can it be?
It's Carnival, it's Carnival,
Oh mother, take me there,
I want to run and sing like them,
And spin round on the fair.
Diddle, diddle, dum dum, diddle diddle dee,
Diddle diddle dum dum, happiness is free!
Monkeys spring and puppets play,
Balloons fly up and far away,
Spinning on the Carousel,
Candy men their sweet-meats sell.
It's Carnival, it's Carnival!

Seals are balancing their balls,
Prizes are won at shooting-malls.
Diddle diddle dum dum, diddle diddle
dee.

Diddle diddle dum dum, happiness is
free.

5th October

Dwarf nose (1)

In a town there once lived a cobbler with
his wife and his son Jacob. They were
very poor, and the wife sold fruit and
vegetables at market, where Jacob often
helped her. One day an old woman they
had never seen before came past the
stall. The ancient woman came up to
them and felt the fruit with her fingers.
Then she rummaged in the cabbages and
held them up to her long nose, but
nothing seemed to suit her. Then she

reached down to the turnips, and Jacob
said to her, "First you touch everything
so that no one else wants to buy them,
and then you don't like anything! Why
don't you bend down your skinny neck
and look at them!" Then the old woman
laughed mockingly and in the end
bought some cabbages, which Jacob
had to help her carry. She led him to a
falling-down house, but when she
opened the door, a bright light shone out.
The house was made of marble and fine
wood, and the sofa he sat on was of
velvet. The old woman began to make
some soup for him, and squirrels and
sea-swine served it to him. He'd never
tasted such lovely soup, but afterwards
the sweet smell of incense made him
drowsy, and in his dreams he thought he
was serving the old lady with the other
animals, and taught him how to cook the
queerest meals. Once he had to stuff a
chicken, and in a little cupboard he found
many herbs that he didn't know. A strong
scent filled his nostrils, the same as when
he had been eating the soup. He sneezed
and then woke up. Shocked over how

long he had been, he rushed back to the market.

His mother was still there. "Are you angry with me, mother?" he asked. The woman turned on him and said, "Go away you ugly dwarf! I don't think that's funny." And she wouldn't have anything to do with him. Distraught, Jacob went to see his father, and there he found out that Jacob had been stolen seven years ago, and when he asked more questions, the man chased him away. At the barber's he looked in the mirror and saw what had happened to him: the old woman had enchanted a long ugly nose onto a round head, and his legs were short and thin. Whatever would become of him now?

6th October

Dwarf nose (2)

Because his parents didn't recognise him now, he wondered what he should do. Then he remembered that he had learned how to cook with the old woman. Wasn't the Duke well-known as a glutton? The

other cooks laughed when they saw him, but they let him cook breakfast for the Duke, just to see what he could do. They put a stool by the oven for him so that he could reach. The Duke noticed straight away that someone else had cooked for him, but because it tasted so good, he employed Jacob, whom he called 'Nose.' Nose cooked so well that soon he took over the whole kitchen, and once he bought three geese from market.

When he got them home, he noticed that one of them sat there and sighed just like a person. It was Mimi, the daughter of a wizard, and she was under a fairy's spell. Nose took her into his room and told her his own story. When a neighbouring Duke came to stay, who was also a glutton, Nose did his best dish. The Duke was full of praise, but he asked him where the Pasta Suzanna was. Nose said he would go and fetch it, but in all truth he didn't know the recipe. Luckily, Mimi

knew, so he prepared the Pasta and took it upstairs. But the Duke said, "You've missed out the Nieselmiesel herb, you stupid dwarf! If you don't cook it properly tomorrow, I'll have your head!" Terrified he went back to Mimi, but Mimi, being a wizard's daughter, new where to find the herb. The next night, when he was cooking it, the smell filled his nostrils,

and before he knew what was happening, he had turned into a handsome young man, for it was the same soup that the witch had given him in the first place! Nose and Mimi ran away and they went to Mimi's father, who changed her back to her real form. Then he went back to his parents and told them his story. They couldn't believe their happiness, and had him tell the story again and again.

Meanwhile, in the Palace, the Duke accused his guest of stealing his cook, and the argument was so great that war was declared, and a long time passed before they made peace again.

7th October

Autumn Wind

The trees are waiting fearfully,
For they know the time has come,
When all the greenness of their lives
Will very soon be done.
And sure enough the Autumn wind
Comes whistling round and round,
And one by one, the clinging leaves
Are torn down to the ground.

8th October

The Way to the Mill

The farmer fetches the donkey Nick out of the stable and lays the carrying-saddle on his back. Lumpy the dog is very pleased and doesn't leave his side. He knows for sure that when the corn is taken to the mill he can go too. He jumps around barking, *"Woof, woof! Haven't*

we got a lovely donkey? Isn't he carrying a heavy sack!" When there's no more people to tell, he tells the rabbits on the fields and the birds in the trees, he's so proud! When they get to the mill, the farmer hands over the corn. They are crushed between the heavy stones and turned into soft white flour. Meanwhile Lumpy has been taking good care of Nick.

He even holds the rope between his teeth so that he can't get away. Now he has to carry the flour back, and he eats thistles along the way, for he needs a lot of nourishment to keep going. Yes, that's how it was a hundred years ago.

9th October

Heidi in a Foreign Land (1)

The first morning Heidi woke up in Frankfurt, she didn't know where she was. Then she remembered, and she jumped out of bed and got dressed. Then she looked out of one of the big windows, but all she could see were walls and windows. Then Miss Tinnet put her head round the door and said, "Breakfast's

ready!" After breakfast, Clara asked her about her own home, and Heidi began to tell her with joy about the mountains, the goats, the meadows, and everything that she loved. Meanwhile Mr. Cummins had come to give the children their lessons, and Miss Rottenmyer led him into the diningroom to tell him how displeased she was with the child she had been sent. But Mr. Cummins didn't want to make any judgements until he had met her, and so he went into the study. Miss Rottenmyer paced the diningroom in great agitation. But suddenly she heard a loud crash from the study and someone calling for Sebastian.

Heidi had thought she could hear some fir-trees rustling like they did in the mountains, and in her excitement in rushing to the window she had taken the tablecloth with her and pulled everything onto the floor. Later, when she met Sebastian in the corridor, she asked him, "Where do you have to go so that you can see right down into the valley?" "You'll have to go to the top of that high tower that you can see out of the window," said Sebastian. Heidi ran out of the door in the direction of the tower, but she went through street after street without coming to it. Then she asked a young boy with a barrel-organ if he could show her the way. "I can," said the boy, "but what will you give me for it?" "What do you

want?" asked Heidi, "A penny," said the boy. Heidi made a deal, Clara was sure to give her the money. Soon they were standing before a Church with a higher tower. Heidi rang the bell and the tower-keeper opened the door. Heidi asked him so nicely to show her the top that he took her by the hand and led her there. But Heidi was disappointed with what she saw, for only houses stretched for miles and miles. But as she was going down she soon cheered up, for she found a family of cats on the stairs.

And when the tower-keeper let her have the kittens, her eyes shone with joy. Outside, the boy was still waiting and Heidi said to him, "Come and fetch your money tomorrow, it's too late now." It was indeed late, as everyone was already sitting at the table. Clara was delighted with the kittens, but Miss Rottenmyer certainly wasn't: "Sebastian, take these horrible animals away!" she cried, and then she went into the study and locked the door. She didn't appear again until bedtime, and she certainly didn't know that the cats were still in the house! Sebastian had put them in a safe place so that the children could sometimes play with them.

Heidi in a Foreign Land (2)

The next day brought even more excitement! In the morning someone rang the bell, and when Sebastian went to open it, there stood a dirty little boy with a barrel-organ saying, "I want to see Clara. She owes me a penny!" Before long Sebastian found out that it was Heidi who owed him the money. Then he smiled and led the boy into the study, where he began to play on his organ, much to the delight of the two girls. "Stop! Stop at once!" cried Miss Rottenmyer as she came running up to the boy, but his tortoise walked in between her legs and sent her screaming into the air.

Sebastian stood at the door doubled up with laughter! After he had managed to control himself, he took the boy out and put two pennies in his hand. "One's for Clara, and one's for your playing," he said. But the excitement of the day still wasn't over. Someone else came to the door with a covered basket addressed to Miss Clara. Sebastian took it into the study where Mr. Cummins had resumed lessons. He had no idea that the contents of the basket was going to mean another shock for Miss Rottenmyer, for when the basket was put on the floor, six little kittens jumped out! The tower-keeper had sent them. Miss Rottenmyer was speechless with horror at first, but then she shouted at the top of her voice, "Miss Tinnet! Sebastian!" They rushed in and managed to get the cats to the place where they had hidden the other kittens. When Miss Rottenmyer had recovered from her shock to a certain extent, she gave Heidi a real talking-to, and if it hadn't been for Clara defending her, she would have been severely punished. After dinner every day, Heidi sat for a few hours alone in her room and thought about home. Her only comfort was that the bread-mountain she was building for gran was getting bigger.

Heidi in a Foreign Land (3)

One afternoon, Heidi felt so homesick that she put the rolls in her big red scarf,

cry, but very quietly so that no one could hear, for she didn't want anyone to think she was ungrateful.

Grandmother gave her one comfort in her sadness: "Whenever you feel unhappy," she said, "And you think you can't turn to anyone, tell everything to God, and then things will work out." So Heidi prayed every night and every morning, but since she still had to stay in Frankfurt, she thought God couldn't have heard her prayers, and so she stopped praying. But something good had happened, Heidi had learned to read! Mr. Cummins could hardly believe it. As a reward she found a wonderful book by her plate one evening. This was Heidi's greatest treasure, and she read the stories again and again.

out on her old hat and went! But she had only reached the door when she met Miss Rottenmyer. The lady was shocked when she saw Heidi dressed to go out, and when she heard that Heidi wanted to go home she didn't know what to do, so she wrote to Clara's grandmother. The grandmother replied and said that she would be arriving the next day, so great preparations were made for her. Heidi was delighted with the old lady and trusted her straight away. After lunch, when everyone else was asleep, Heidi went into her room and read the big picture book that gran had brought with her. Grandmother was astonished when she discovered that Heidi couldn't read. She also noticed how Heidi got sadder and paler every day. At night Heidi often couldn't sleep, and when she finally did she dreamed of the mountains, the goats and her grandad. When she woke up and thought she was in her little straw bed she always found herself instead in the big bed in Frankfurt. Then she would bury her face in her pillow and cry and

12th October

Candy Land

Come with me to Candy Land!
Bring your spoon and plate,
For we can eat all day there,
And dance 'til it gets late.
The fountains are of lemonade,
The flowers are all nice sweets,
Pink strawberry cakes grow there on trees
And the grass is all sweet-meat.

The waitresses are fairies,
They bathe you in soft foam,
And the carriages are driven
By giggling little gnomes.
The pixies close your tired eyes
And spin you happy dreams,
They cushion you with pillows gold
And sheets of emerald green.
In Candy Land for breakfast,
They give you tender goose,
And when the dream is over,
You can't shake the memory loose.

13th October

Lumpy and his Friends

It takes Lumpy a long time to say good day to all his friends in the morning. "*Moo!*" says Lena the cow, and as she turns round her little bell jingles. Lisa the calf would like to go for a run on the meadow, but the farmer's wife will soon be coming with some food, and he mustn't miss that! "*Coo, coo,*" say the pigeons. Lumpy walks peacefully by

them, for he knows he mustn't chase them. The ducks by the pond haven't got any time for Lumpy today, for mother duck is teaching them how to swim and dive and how to hide in the reeds if they have to. For ducks have quite a few enemies, and because of this, father duck is always on the look out for anything that wants to harm his children. Fiona, the lady duck, wants to catch a butterfly, but the butterfly floats gracefully away, just like the dragon-fly that one of the little ducks tries to catch. Then Lumpy sees his favourite playmate over in the enclosure, Hammie the foal. Barking, the dog chases over the meadow, and Hammie comes whinneying towards him. They chase each other until Hammie has had enough and goes back to his mother.

14th October

The White Dove

Before the Palace of the King stood a fine pear tree, which produced the most beautiful fruit each year. But when they were ripe, the pears were all picked in one night, and no one knew who had one it. Now the King had three sons, the youngest of whom was the most stupid, and so he was called Simpleton. The King ordered his eldest son to stay under the tree for a whole year, so that he was bound to catch the thief. When the fruit got ripe, he had only to stay under the tree one more night, for the next morning they would be picked. But when it came to this time the son fell asleep, and by morning all the pears were gone. The same thing happened to the second son when it was his turn. When it was now up to Simpleton, the whole Court laughed, but Simpleton fought to stay awake, and this is what he saw: a white dove came and took the pears one by one. When she took the last one, Simpleton followed her to a high mountain, where the dove disappeared into a cave. Simpleton looked around him, and saw a little man. "God bless you," said Simpleton. "God blessed me the moment you spoke!" said the little man. "You have saved me! Go down into the cave and you shall find your fortune!"

Simpleton went into the cave, where many steps led right down. When he got to the bottom, he saw the white dove completely stuck in a spider's web. But, as she saw him, she broke loose, and when she had torn the last feather from the web, she turned into a beautiful Princess. Simpleton took her to his father, and she happily agreed to be his wife. The weddding was greatly celebrated, and when the King died, Simpleton inherited the Kingdom and became a wise and powerful King.

The Puppet Saves the Princess

Felix has got a puppet-theatre for his birthday. He likes the little Princess best. She's got a face like an apple and is called Rosie. Before going to bed Felix puts his old friend Sambo the monkey into the cupboard because he's dirty. "That's sad," says Rosie. During the night the King wakes up, and so he says, "Rosie, sing me a lullaby!" But the princess has disappeared. "Perhaps the crocodile's taken her – or the robber, or the witch!" says the puppet, "I'll look for her until I find her! We'll have to use Felix's aeroplane!" So Felix and the puppet fly to Africa to ask the crocodile, but he's got toothache and hasn't eaten for days. So they fly on to the black forest where the robber hides out. "But suppose the robber has hidden Rosie in his cave?"
"Think, think!" says the puppet, "If the robber has hidden her, then he'll stay at home, but if we can find him, then he hasn't hidden her!" So he and Felix dress up as robbers. "Hello, brother!" says the puppet to his robber friend. "We're going to steal Princess Rosie, are you coming?" "Ha, Ha!" laughed the robber, "It's not every day you steal a Princess! I'm coming with you!" "Aha!" exclaimed Felix and the puppet, and off they went.

Then they flew to the witch's house, but the witch knew nothing of a Princess called Rosie, so the two flew quickly back home. The puppet began to open every door in the house looking for Rosie, and the King had to sneeze twelve times because of the draught. As he was complaining he suddenly stopped: "Listen!" he whispered, "I can hear Rosie singing!" The puppet had just opened the cupboard door, and there was Rosie singing and dancing with the monkey! "I was comforting Sambo because Felix had locked him in the cupboard." Then Felix was ashamed and went red. The

King reached in his pocket and pulled out a thick medal for the puppet, as a reward for rescuing the Princess.

16th October

The Two Hares

Between the mountain and deep, deep valley,
There once sat two fine hares,
They ate up all the green, green grass
They ate up all the green, green grass,
'Til someone saw them there,
'Til someone saw them there.

Now when they were quite fully full,
The two hares they sat down,
Then the big bad hunter came,
Then the big bad hunter came,
And gaily shot them down,
And gaily shot them down.
From the shock they then recovered,
And soon they realised,
That they were still alive, alive,
That they were still alive, alive,
And ran to save their lives,
And ran to save their lives.

17th October

Rescue From the Swamp

Once when I wanted to cross a swamp, i was much broader than I thought, so moved back to get a better run-up, but was unlucky and didn't jump far enough finding myself stuck in the swamp. I would certainly have died if I hadn't pulled myself out with my plait. I saved the horse too, for I had clung onto him with my knees.

Sweet Porridge

Once a girl lived with her mother, and there came a time when they didn't have anything left to eat, so the girl went into the wood. Here she met an old woman who gave her a little pot. She was to say to the pot, "Cook, pot!" and then the pot would cook sweet porridge. When she said "Stand, pot!" then it would stop cooking. The girl took the pot home, and from then on they could eat as much porridge as they wanted. Once, when the girl had gone out, her mother said, "Cook, pot!" and she ate her fill. But when she had eaten, she forgot the word for stopping it, and so the porridge flowed over into the kitchen and spread out all over the house. Then it ran from one house to another until the whole street was full. When there was only one house left, the girl came home and was able to stop it by saying, "Stand, pot!" Then when anyone wanted to go into town, they had to eat their way through the porridge.

19th October

Rennie the Fox (1)

On a fine spring day, King Noble was holding Court. All the animals were invited, except Rennie, for everyone had

another of his tricks to report. Graham his nephew was the only one there to defend him. Then the King sent Brown the bear to fetch Rennie so that he could defend himself.

When Brown appeared, Rennie complained, "Oh! I've ruined my insides with honey!" Brown pricked up his ears. "Honey? he said. "Do you want some?" said Rennie. "Then come with me!" He led Brown to a split tree where he had hidden some wedges. "The honey's in there," he said. When the bear put in his snout, Rennie gave him a push, pulled the wedges and shut the bear in.

20th October

Rennie the Fox (2)

The wolf's stomach was rumbling, and Rennie said to him, "The farmer's larder is full of ham, and what's more, there's a

hole in the wall where you can get in!'' Already the wolf's mouth began to water. As soon as they got inside the larder, they tucked into the ham, and while the wolf ate, Rennie kept slipping out to make sure no one was coming, or so he said. Suddenly he dropped a knife which woke the farmer, and while Rennie escaped the wolf was still struggling to get through the wall, but now he was too fat! The farmer got him before he could escape.

21st October

Rennie the Fox (3)

When the King heard what had happened to Brown the bear after he had managed to free himself, he was very angry. But perhaps Molly the sly cat would succeed in fetching Rennie. Rennie again tried to tempt her with honey, but she would have preferred a fat little mouse.
Rennie took her to a barn which was supposed to be full of mice. He knew where it was, for he'd stolen a hen here the night before. "Creep in," he said, "I'll

stay here and keep watch.'' Scarcely had Molly put her head in the chink when a noose caught her round the neck. ''Is that how you sing while you're eating!'' laughed Rennie, and he ran off.

22nd October

Rennie the Fox (4)

Graham his nephew was the only one who finally managed to bring Rennie to the Court. All the animals brought so many cases against him that the King decided to hang him. There were so many accusations that the fox had difficulty defending himself, but he pleaded not guilty. But the wolf said,

''Listen, Your Majesty, to the terrible things Rennie has done to me and my wife! Once on a meadow, a mare was grazing with her calves. Rennie told me that she''d certainly give me a ride, all I had to do was get on. But when I tried, she gave me an almighty kick, and there I was doubled up in pain while Rennie was doubled up with laughter. Once when he had fallen into a well, he told my wife to lower herself down on the other bucket so that he would come up. After she had so kindly done this, he laughed down at her and ran away!

Rennie threw you a crate of fish from a moving carriage, risking his life, and you ate all the fish, leaving him only the bones! And that's not all I know about you!'' With cunning and lies Rennie handled his case so well that the King set him free. Whistling happily he set off home. On they way he met Ben the ram and Les the hare and he politely invited them to walk with him a little way. When they got to the fox's house, Rennie asked the hare to come and say hello to his wife, but Ben was to stay outside. As soon as

It wasn't until much later that I found her. Another time he told my wife to go fishing with her tail, but because it was so cold her tail got frozen in the water and we had to cut off a part to set her free! Such crimes must be punished!''

23rd October

Rennie the Fox (5)

But then Graham said, ''Be quiet, you! You're no better! What about the time

they were in the house, Rennie tore off the hare's head, put it in a bag and gave it to the ram saying, ''Take this to the King quickly! It's got an important message for him, but you'd better not read it yourself!'' Ben did as he was told.

But when the King opened the bag, he had the ram killed, for he thought he was guilty. Grim the wolf was still furious with Rennie, and he challenged him to a duel before the King's throne. The fox won, but only with cunning: he threw so much sand into the wolf's eyes with his tail that he was in so much pain he had to give in. Then the King thought that he could use Rennie's talents in politics and, full of joy, the Redtail family had a big celebration.

The Tired Village

Everyone goes to bed at night,
The beggar and the King,
The village closes sleepy eyes
Like the birds under their wings.

The moon slides with its silvery glance
Over Palace, Church and barn,
And the children are tucked up in bed,
To shelter them from harm.

The pigeons' "Coos" are long since still,
The dogs no longer bark,
The swallows slumber in their nests,
Surrounded by the dark,

The donkey's dreaming in his stall,
The pigs snore on the ground,
And only the hands upon the clock
Keep turning round and round.

The Wooden Carousel

Night is spreading over the fairground, and evening is the best time, for it's the busiest time. Only one corner of the fair is quiet, for there stands an old wooden carousel. Deserted, the wooden horses, zebras and pigs turn around in circles to the music from the old barrel-organ. "I could cry when I think of how the children loved to sit on my back!" says a wooden horse. "We've got to get away from here!" squeaks a wooden pig, and since everyone agrees, when the fair closes for the night, they all spring down and run away. For a long time they wander through unknown streets until they come to a house with a big garden, and a notice saying "Town Orphanage" on the door.

"I wonder if there are any children here who'd like to play with us," said a Zebra. "I think we should stay here for the night anyway." So each animal found a place to stand. What a welcome they got in the morning as the children clambered all over them in disbelief when they came into the garden! The wooden animals had never been so much appreciated. And so there they live to this day, happy and newly-painted!

26th October

The Three Brothers

There was once a man who had three sons, and his only possession was the house they lived in.

Now each one would have liked to inherit the house, but the father loved each one equally. So he said to them, "Each of you must go out into the world and learn a trade, and the one that makes the best masterpiece shall have the house." So away they went. One became a blacksmith, the other a barber, and the third a fencing master. When they had nothing left to learn, they all went home. Since none of them knew how to demonstrate their arts, they sat down and thought. Suddenly a hare came running over the field. "Just what we need!" cried the barber, so he took a basin and some soap, and shaved the rabbit while it was still running, without cutting it or hurting it in any way. Before long a man came by in a cart who was being chased. The blacksmith ran after the horse, tore off its old shoes and gave him four new shoes while it was still running. The father was delighted with his two son's abilities, and now it was the third one's turn. When it began to rain, he took his sword, and swung it so skilfully around his head that not a single drop of rain touched him. His father was amazed and said, "You have easily achieved the

best masterpiece, the house is yours!" The other two brothers were pleased to agree, but because they loved each other so much, they all lived in the house anyway, and because they were so skilled at their crafts, they earned a lot of money. When they were all old, one of the brothers died, and the other two were so heartbroken that they died soon afterwards. And because everyone knew how much they had loved each other, they were all laid in one grave.

27th October

The Seven Dwarfs (1)

Behind the seven mountains under seven fir-trees stood a little house. It was seven foot high and seven foot wide. Every morning after sunrise, seven windows opened and the big wooden front door opened. But out marched only six dwarfs. Two carried spades, three carried hoes and one carried a lantern. So they plodded through dark woods up to the seven mountains, to their seven workshops. One dug for diamonds, one for gold, one for silver, one for copper, one for rubies and the last one for emeralds. In the seventh mountain was a coalmine, but this was closed. Now the six dwarfs could have been very happy together, but every time they walked through the wood, from every corner someone said, "Where's the seventh dwarf? There's always seven dwarfs!"

This, of course, annoyed the six dwarfs very much. One day they'd had enough of it, so they decided to look for a seventh dwarf. On a thick oaktree by a crossroads they pinned this notice: "DWARF REQUIRED, APPLY TO THE SIX DWARFS."

The Seven Dwarfs (2)

Soon they had their first applicant, but when he discovered he would have to be the seventh dwarf and work in the coalmine he went away saying, "I'm not going down a dirty hole!
You can fetch your own coal!"
And this was the reaction of many others. "Yes," said one of them, "Ever since people read the story of Snow-white, they always think there should be seven dwarfs!" "I know!" said another one, "We'll put an advert in the paper!" And so they did. A garden-gnome also read the advert, and he gave up his job, loaded his belongings onto a little cart and set off for the seven mountains. All the animals were very helpful to him, and after six days he eventually reached the house "Here I am!" called the garden gnome,

"Will you take me as your seventh dwarf?" The six dwarfs were very pleased, for the gnome didn't even mind having to do the dirtiest job. So the seven dwarfs marched happily off to work every day, and no one had any reason to mock them now.

The Lion and the Crocodile

Once while hunting I got impossibly lost: Before me was a rushing river, behind me an abyss. I turned around and saw the gaping mouth of a crocodile, I turned to the river and saw a lion ready to spring. Terrified I threw myself to the ground and waited for my end. Nothing happened — the lion had sprung into the crocodile's mouth!

Stephen is in Luck (1)

Stephen had served his master faithfully for seven years, but now he wanted to go home to his mother. "You have served me well," said his master, "And I am going to pay you well." And he gave Stephen a lump of gold as big as his head. On his way home he met a man galloping along on his horse. "A horse would be a fine thing," thought Stephen. "You can sit on it like a chair, save your shoes and move quicker." When the man discovered Stephen had a lump of gold, he offered to sell him his horse for it. The deal was made. Stephen felt much lighter now without the gold and galloped away, but suddenly the horse reared and threw him into a ditch. As Stephen rose from the ditch, groaning, he saw a farmer with a cow. He said to the farmer, "Riding's no fun when you can break your neck."

"I'd rather have your cow, because then you can get milk, butter, cheese — and peace!" The farmer laughed and swapped his cow for the horse. But later when Stephen got thirsty and tried to milk the cow, she kicked him with her hind legs with such force that he was knocked unconscious. Luckily a butcher came along who had a young pig in his cart. The butcher helped Stephen up, and Stephen said to him, "I don't think I'll be able to do anything with this cow, but I wouldn't mind having some sausages from that pig!" Of course the butcher was only too pleased to exchange the pig for the cow. Further on, Stephen met a young boy with a goose under his arm, and Stephen told him what luck he'd had with his exchanges. Then the boy began to make his mouth water at the thought of the goose, but Stephen preferred to keep his pig, then the boy said, "A pig has just been stolen from the Mayor, and if anyone finds you with your pig, they might accuse you! I tell you what! I'll give you the goose and you give me the pig!" Stephen thought that was very nice of the boy, so he set off home with the goose under his arm.

31st October

Stephen is in Luck (2)

Stephen was glad that he was nearly home, but as he was going through the last village, he met a knife-grinder, who was joyfully singing in his work. "It must be a good job you have if it makes you so happy," said Stephen. "Yes, working with your hands is very rewarding," said the man, "but where did you get that lovely goose from?" Then Stephen told him of all the exchanges he had made, and the man praised him. But then he said, "But have you always got money in your pocket?" "No, not always," said Stephen. "Then you must become a knife-grinder, then you'll never want for anything, and all you need is a grinding-stone. Why don't you swap your goose for my stone?" said the man. "What a wonderful thought," said Stephen, "always to have money in your pocket. This must be my lucky day, everything's going my way!" And happy as a sand boy, he handed over the goose, picked up the heavy stone and set off again. Eventually he got tired, for he'd been up since daybreak and the stone was so heavy. Then he thought how good it would be if he didn't have anything to carry. He came to a fountain and laid the stone on the fountain's edge, then he got down and tried to drink.

He accidentally knocked the stone so that it fell in, and as he saw it sink down, Stephen jumped for joy and thanked God for freeing him from his heavy load. "I'm the luckiest person in the world!" he cried, and he ran all the way home to his mother.

1st November

The Dear Little Sunny Ray

November storms now rule the sea,
The cold north-wind's blasts rave,
Darkness rules now all day long,
As the wind whips up the waves.
Little Tina stays inside,
And with her toys she plays,
Where's our little smiling face,
Our happy sunny ray?

2nd November

Princess Mouseskin

There was once a King who had three daughters, and he wanted to know which one loved him best. So he brought them before him and asked them. The oldest one said she loved him more than the whole Kingdom, the second one said she loved him more than all the precious stones in the world, but the third one said she loved him more than salt. The King was angry with his youngest daughter that she should compare him with such a worthless thing. He gave her one servant and then turned her out into the wood where the servant was to kill her. But when they were in the wood, the Princess asked the servant for mercy. He remained faithful to her and wanted to stay and serve her, but the Princess only asked him for a dress made of mouse-skin, and when he had made her one, she went on her way alone. She went to another King pretending she was a boy and asked him to employ her, and he did. One day his servant brought him a ring that Mouseskin had lost, and the King thought it must be stolen. When the King asked Mouseskin where he had got the ring, she knew she couldn't hide any longer, so she wriggled out of the skin and let her golden hair flow down her back. The King was so overcome by her beauty that he took the crown from his head, placed it on her and asked her to marry him. Mouseskin's father was also invited to the wedding, but he didn't recognise his daughter. All the dishes presented to him were unsalted, and he cried out angrily, "I'd rather die than eat anything without salt!" Then the new Queen leaned over to him and said, "Now you say you'd rather not live without salt, but once you wanted to kill me because I said I loved you more than salt!" Then the King recognised his daughter and asked her for forgiveness. It was worth more than his Kingdom or all the precious stones in the world that he had found her again.

3rd November

The Little Chimney-sweep (1)

At first there were seven chimney-sweeps, and all seven had fine black hats. Every day they cleaned the many chimneys in the town, until one day the smallest one — yes, but that's a long story. So, the smallest one climbed onto the roof of a rather old house and pushed his broom down into the chimney, pulling it out after the normal time. But what was that! He had pulled out a smashing yellow hat! He just couldn't understand it. This was a normal house with normal people, or was it? He didn't know that a wizard had once lived there, and that one day, when he wasn't concentrating, he had put his hat into the chimney rather than in the cupboard. Because the little chimney-sweep didn't know that it was a magic hat, he put it on. Suddenly he felt very tired, so he went straight home and went to sleep. But the hat had the power to grant any wish that the wearer might make. The little sweep had always wanted to travel out into the wide world, but had never had enough money. However, he always dreamed about it. "How I'd love to be in New York . . ." *Wham!* There he is. But all this traffic and noise! No, it's not so nice here, Spain must be nicer. *Wham!* He's already there. Pedro and Dolores greet the little man. Pedro has such lovely black curly hair, almost like a negro – but *they* live in Africa. *Wham* There he is in Africa! How strong Rani the elephant is, how funny

Bum the monkey is, and how astonished the little coloured children are at their strange guest. Now he's hungry. "How I'd love one of my Aunty Nellie's apple pies," he thinks. *Wham!* It's already in his hand at the table at his aunt's house.

4th November

The Little Chimney-sweep (2)

Now I've almost seen the whole world, thought the little chimney sweep, except for China – *Wham!* There he is. A fine Chinese lady is driving in a carriage, and she invites the little sweep onto her house-boat, which is called a junk. Here

because it had fallen from his head. The little sweep quickly got up, he had to get back to work. When he met his six friends, he proudly told them of his adventures and of all the places he had been. The other sweeps listened spellbound, until one of them saw the yellow hat. "That belongs to the wizard, it's a magic hat!" he cried. That explained everything, and all six went to the flat where the wizard lived. The wizard had already missed his hat, and how glad he was to have it back. In his gratitude, he wished a huge cake onto the table and what a feast it made. I wish I'd been there!

he eats lovely food, but not with a knife and fork, with chopsticks. Afterwards, fine tea is passed around in little cups. In China, day is dawning, and when the sun tickles him on the nose he sneezes, and off comes the hat, almost falling into the water. So that was the end of the sweep's world travels. The sun was shining in through his window and a little bird was twittering a happy song. The magic powers of the hat had been broken

The Hard-working Shoe-shiner

Every morning, up at eight,
Peter the shoe-boy comes,
And sitting on his door-step,
He works and gaily hums.
Every brush is in its place,
The cloths are standing by,
His hands so skilfully reach for them,
As over the shoes they fly.

Brown polish, blue polish, yellow too,
He hasn't time to talk,
'Til all the shoes are shining bright,
Ready to go for a walk.

6th November

The wind-maker

When I was with my crew in Egypt, such a strong storm blew up that I was afraid of being torn down into the waves with all my people and animals.

On one side of us stood seven windmills, and not far away was a fat man holding down his right nostril. As soon as he saw our predicament, he blew through his left nostril into our sails and blew us away from the storm.

7th November

The Three Lazy People

A King had three sons whom he loved equally, so he didn't know which one to leave his Kingdom to when he died. When he got ill and knew his end was near, he had his sons brought before him and said, "I have come to the conclusion that whichever one of you is the laziest shall inherit the Kingdom." So the eldest son said, "then you should give it to me, for when I want to go to sleep and a fly lands on my face, I'm too lazy to swot it away." But the second son said, "You should give it to me, for when I'm warming myself by the fire, I let my heels burn before I can be bothered to draw my legs away."

But the third one said, "The Kingdom is definitely mine, for if I was about to be hanged and already had the noose around my neck, if someone then gave me a sharp knife to cut myself free, I would rather hang than go the effort of raising my hand!" When the King heard that he said, "You shall be King!"

8th November

Heidi Goes Home (1)

In reality, Heidi wanted for nothing in Frankfurt. She had nice clothes, she always had the best food to eat. Clara

201

Bravely they looked out into the corridor, and the door was already open and, what was worse, there stood a white figure, and a shiver ran down their backs. When Miss Rottenmyer was told, she wrote a long letter to Clara's father. Two days later he was ringing loudly at the doorbell, and the servants feared it was the ghost playing his tricks before night time! Sebastian took courage and opened the door, and there stood Clara's father — no ghost. He greeted him abruptly and went straight upstairs to his daughter's room. Clara greeted her father with tears of joy and relief, for she was terrified at the thought of the ghost. "We'll soon catch this ghost!" he promised.

was always good to her and Sebastian was a trusted friend. She had also learned to read, and had learned a lot more than that. But her face got paler and paler, and her legs thinner. When grandmother went away again, she became even quieter and tossed and turned in her bed. Miss Rottenmyer noticed how she wandered round the house, and Miss Tinnet had become a lot more gentle with Heidi, since her manner had often made life difficult for Heidi. Then something very strange started to happen in the household: every morning when the servants came down, the front door was always wide open, but no one was to be seen, and nothing was ever stolen. So, in the end, the carriage-driver and Sebastian decided to spend the night in the room near the front door. Unfortunately they fell asleep and didn't wake up until the clock struck one.

Heidi Goes Home (2)

Clara's father sent Sebastian for his old friend Doctor Collins, who had cared for Clara for many years. That evening they both sat in the room where Sebastian and the carriage driver had sat before, and they were more successful. They took hold of the white figure who had been opening the door every night. It turned around and let out a soft cry. There, in her bare feet and white nightdress, stood Heidi.

Looking at them with a confused expression on her face she was shivering from head to foot. "What on earth are you doing, child? Why did you come down?" asked Clara's father. Pale as death Heidi said in an expressionless voice, "I don't know!" Then Dr. Collins said, "You haven't done anything wrong. Now just tell me where you were going." "I wasn't going anywhere," said Heidi. "And I didn't go down by myself, I just suddenly found myself there." "Were you dreaming about anything?" asked Dr. Collins. "Oh, only what I always dream about," said Heidi, "I always dream I'm at grandad's and I open the back door to run out to the fir trees, but when I open the door I'm still in Frankfurt." Then Heidi burst out crying. The good Doctor got up and said, "Cry it all out for a little while, it'll do you good. Everything will be alright in the morning." And he went back to Clara's father. "Your little visitor has been sleepwalking," said Dr. Collins, "she's become ill with homesickness.

You can see how much weight she's lost. The best thing you can do is let her go back to the mountains first thing tomorrow. That is my only remedy." Clara's father was deeply shocked. "Is it really that bad?" he said. "then it must be dealt with immediately!" He went straight to Miss Rottenmyer's room and banged on the door. "Hurry up!" he called. "A journey must be prepared now!" While Miss Rottenmyer was frantically getting dressed, Clara's father rang every bell in the house to get the servants up. One by one they stumbled down and were given their orders. Clara had been woken up by the noise and wanted to know what was going on. When her father explained who the real ghost was and that Heidi was very ill, Clara sadly had to agree to what was

unavoidable. Meanwhile day had broken, and Heidi stood there in her Sunday clothes not knowing what was happening. She wondered what was in the big chest that was standing in the room. "Heidi, aren't you pleased?" asked Sebastian. Heidi looked at him blankly. "Don't you know!" exclaimed Sebastian, "You're going home, today, now!" "Home?" repeated Heidi, and she just could not grasp it.

10th November

Heidi Goes Home (3)

At first Heidi couldn't believe it, but when she saw the fresh bread-rolls for gran, the sausages for Peter and the tobacco for grandad, she got more and more excited. Packing was such fun that Clara almost forgot how sad she was that Heidi was going, and when the cry, "The carriage is ready!" came, there was not time to cry. Sebastian went with her to the station in the little village. He couldn't manage the climb all the way up the mountain, so Heidi went up on her own. All the way

along people flocked round her asking questions, but she pushed on through the crowds until she reached Peter's cottage. She sprang in through the door and stood there, completely out of breath. "Good gracious!" said gran. "That's just how Heidi used to burst in. If only it was her." "it is me, gran!" cried Heidi and she rushed over to grandmother and threw herself at her feet. For a while she was so overwhelmed she couldn't say a word, but then she opened up her bag and pulled out all the fresh bread rolls onto gran's lap, for Clara had given her fresh ones for the others she had collected over that long time. "Now I've got to run and see grandfather," said Heidi. "I'll come back soon!"

Heidi ran the rest of the way up the mountain, and before long she could see the fir-trees hovering over the roof and the little house, in front of which sat grandfather on a bench. Heidi dashed up to him, threw her basket on the floor and threw her arms around him, and through sheer excitement she was speechless. Grandad didn't say anything either, but for the first time in many, many years, tears came to his eyes. That night Heidi slept the whole night through. She was home again, in the mountains.

11th November

Heidi is Happy (1)

So now Heidi was home again, but she had learned a lot during her stay in Frankfurt. She had learned how to read, and also she had learned to have faith in

God, for Clara's grandmother was a religious lady. Now every day Heidi could read to gran out of the old song-book, and she even managed to persuade her grandad to have faith in God and people. Next Sunday he went to Church with her, and he was amazed how everyone was so pleased to see him, and the Priest was most pleased of all. He shook grandad's hand again and again and didn't want to let it go. Then winter came, and Olaf wanted to spend winter down in the

village with Heidi and the goats. He found room for his goats in someone's stall, and for him and Heidi he had rented some of the many winter rooms in the village. What Heidi liked best of all was the living room with the tiled stove, behind which she made her bed. She certainly wouldn't get cold here!

12th November

Heidi is Happy (2)

Peter was glad that Heidi was spending winter in the village, for it got harder and harder to get up the mountain to visit her. But he wasn't pleased that Heidi went to school now, for now she always knew when Peter played truant. One day she said to him, "Aren't you ashamed that you still can't read?" "It's too hard," sighed Peter. "No it's not," said Heidi,

"And if you don't start learning the alphabet I'll tell grandad you've been playing truant." Peter didn't want that to happen, for he had great respect for Olaf. So from then on the children studied every day, and in fact, before long Peter could read. The school-teacher couldn't believe it! Peter could read! At last winter was over, and Heidi and grandad went back up the mountain. One day heidi got a letter from Clara, who said that she was coming to visit Heidi for a few days, and one day Heidi saw a strange carriage coming up the mountain.

It was Clara in a carrying-chair, her grandmother and people carrying bags. "It's them, it's them!" cried Heidi, and soon she had her arms around her friend. Grandmother went back to the town in the evening for she had friends there. Peter was terribly jealous, for now Heidi didn't have time for him, for the two girls were always either writing letters or

playing with the goats together. But Clara was getting stronger from day to day, and soon her cheeks were as rosy as Heidi's. She got a good appetite, and grandad looked with pleasure at his young guest. Every morning when drinking the healthy goatmilk, she would ask, "May I have a drop more, please?"

13th November

Heidi is Happy (3)

Clara had now been on the mountains for two weeks, and one evening grandad said, "Tomorrow we'll all go with the goats onto the meadow." Heidi was so overjoyed that she went and called to Peter, "Peter, tomorrow we're coming with you onto the meadow all day!" But Peter wasn't so pleased, for Heidi still

wouldn't have any time for him. The next day when he got to Olaf's cottage and saw Clara's wheelchair before him, he gave it an almighty kick which sent it flying down the slope.

Then he disappeared as though he hadn't done it. Now he thought that Clara wouldn't be able to stay any longer, but he was wrong. Grandfather carried Clara up onto the meadow, and he informed the Police-Inspector in Frankfurt about the wheelchair and asked him to investigate it. Peter was frightened. When Olaf had gone again, Heidi wanted to show Clara something, but she couldn't walk. "Just hang onto me and Peter," encouraged Heidi. "It must quite easy." Clara walked rather slowly and clumsily, but she walked. With every step Clara got more confident, Peter had a long face, but what could he do? When Clara's father paid an unexpected visit and asked Peter the way, Peter flew off in fear down the mountain, for he thought he was the Police Inspector from Frankfurt. What a surprise her father got when he came to Olaf's cottage. This healthy girl walking with Heidi's aid was his daughter? Then her grandmother came, and her eyes sparkled with happiness. No one had expected this. In the evening they all sat down together and celebrated this near-miracle.

The Frightened Hare

There was once a hare who slept under a palm-tree. Suddenly he woke up and thought, what would happen if the world fell down? At this moment a monkey dropped a coconut from a tree.

Shocked, the hare sprang away, "Save yourself while you can!" he cried, "the world has fallen down!" Another hare saw him bolting away and called, "Why are you running so fast?" "Don't you know! The world's fallen down!"

This went on until there were a hundred hares running along trying to save their lives. Soon all the animals in the wood had found out and started running with them. When the King of the wood saw them, he put himself in their way and stopped them. "Why are you running away?" he asked. "the world's fallen down!" they cried. "Who's seen it?" asked the King. "I haven't," said the elephant. "Ask the fox." And all the way down the line the animals asked each other. When it at last reached the hare, he told them what had happened to him, so the lion went to the palm-tree with the hare, and there they found the coconut. which is just as well, as otherwise they would have been running to this day.

15th November

Himplebum and Pimplebum

Himplebum and Pimplebum
Climb panting up the hill,
They have to stop and rest a while
Or the air will make them ill.
But this they've done for eighty years,
And will for many more,
For the only pastime of their life
Is to climb up there and snore!

16th November

The Carnation

There was once a King who never wanted to get married. But once he saw a girl going into Church who was so beautiful that he married her. After a year she gave birth to a son, and the King said, "The first person I meet on the street shall be his godfather." He went out, and the first person he met was a poor old man. When the King asked him if he would be the godfather of his child, the man said yes, as long as he could take him to Church on his own. But the King had a wicked gardener, who hid himself in the Church between the pews. The gardener heard the old man take him to the Altar, bless him and give him the gift of having all his wishes come true. Now the wicked gardener wanted to have the child, so one day while the Queen was walking in the garden with it, he snatched the child away and smeared the Queen's mouth with blood.

Then he went to the King and told him how he had seen the Queen kill the child and eat it. The King threw the Queen into prison, but the gardener sent the child a long way away to live with a forester. Now the forester had a beautiful daughter called Colleen, and they fell in love. The Prince told her where he came from, and that all his wishes came true. Soon afterwards the gardener came, but the Prince turned him into a poodle. He turned Colleen into a carnation, and presented himself to the King as a hunter. He demanded no wages, but just a room of his own which he could lock. One of his friends thought this was rather strange, so he followed him and peeped through the keyhole. There he saw the hunter sitting at a finely-decked table with a beautiful lady by his side. The man thought he must be a very rich man, so while they were hunting together he attacked the Prince, but all he found on his person was a carnation. This they took to the King. When the hunter got back, he demanded to get back his carnation. When the King refused, the Prince revealed himself as his son and the Carnation as Colleen, the girl he loved. When the King heard this he was overjoyed and he released the Queen from prison. Colleen married the Prince, but the gardener was sentenced to being a poodle for the rest of his life.

17th November

The Ride on the Cannon-ball

Once, when we wanted to occupy a town, the Field Marshall wanted to know what the situation was like in the town. So I sat on a cannon ball and was fired right into the fortess. But as I was flying through

the air, I began to wonder if the enemy would be willing to fire me back, so I hopped onto a ball that the enemy had just fired and plopped right back into our own camp.

18th November

The Laughing Gnome

There is a laughing gnome-man,
Who comes round in our crowd,
"Three times seven is 21!"
He always cried out loud.
With his nonsense-words we have our fill,
And so we cry, "Gnome! Please be still!"

19th November

The Little Locomotive (1)

The little locomotive is at home at the station. She pushes the waggons to and fro, and only has a break when she needs to eat coal and drink water. This is her life, and she's very happy because she's so useful. One day three workers came. The first one knocked all around her and said,

"It rattles." And the second one examined her boiler saying, "She's too old, we'll have to turn her into scrap metal."
The third one said, "We'll do it first thing tomorrow." "Scrap-metal," thought the engine sadly, "that will mean the end of

me." And so at night she secretly rolled over the lines into the wood. She's free! Under a tree she dreams of her future adventures.

20th November

The Little Locomotive (2)

In the morning when the little engine woke up in the wood, she saw a pretty farmhouse on the wood's edge. The farmer and his wife were just having breakfast. They were amazed when an engine looked in through the window and said, "Excuse me, do you have room for me?" They were very surprised, but because she was a polite engine, they said, "There should be some room for you in the stable over there." Noreen the

horse was also very surprised, but afterwards she was pleased to have a visitor, for she had a big secret to tell. "I was once a circus horse," she said. "I don't like farm work, I want to go back to the circus Apollo." "Oh, but I think you're better off here," said the engine anxiously. But the next morning Noreen had disappeared. The farm people were very sad, for now without a horse they can't plough the field, "Excuse me," said the engine, "but supposing I plough your field. I'm even stronger than a horse." The farmers, of course, agreed at once, and ploughing a field is no different from running along a train line for the engine. So she helped the farmers for many days, and as payment she got two tons of coal, then she puffed off towards the town.

The Little Locomotive (3)

This is the first time the engine had ever been to a town, and there she met a tram. Because she was dirty from her work on the farm, the conductor laughed, "You've come straight from the coal-cellar into town, aren't you ashamed of yourself?" But then the tram broke down and the conductor couldn't find what was wrong with it. But of course the engine came to the rescue, and attached herself to the tram, taking the work-people wherever they want to go. Then the conductor apoligised, but the engine was very hurt and wondered how she could get clean. The sea, of course, would be a wonderful way of getting clean! So off she puffed to the sea. She tried the water at first to make sure it wasn't too cold, but it was alright, so she rolled in deeper and deeper. How pleased the other bathers were. What fun it was to splash around in the water and giggle because it tickled you.

The fish were too afraid to come out, especially when the engine was playing handball with the boys and kept coughing when the water went down her funnel. No one had ever had so much fun at the seaside. When the engine got out, she shook herself like a dog to get dry. Then back she went into the water and scored a goal with her nose, 1:0 to the engine. Then she dived down under the waves like a submarine. By this time the beachguards had had enough and said, "That's enough now, you're spotlessly clean." When the engine heard that, she was very glad and swam out of the water. Yes, she was sparkling clean, she hadn't been so clean since the day she'd been made. After a happy whistle she trundled off.

The Little Locomotive (4)

The little engine went off to the other town on the other side of the coast. But something happened here that the engine did not expect. As she was going round the corner, a car appeared, driven by two men from her old station, the two men who had wanted to turn her into scrap-metal! And they had recognised her. Full of fear she turned on full steam and ran away, but the men chased her, and what a wild chase it was! The engine started billowing out the blackest smoke to give herself a shield, and the men got

completely lost, and they went huffing and puffing up and down the street, not catching a glimpse of the engine. The little engine hardly dared to puff as she hid between the houses. One of her wheels had become loose and her piston hurt, since, after all, she was no spring chicken. Eventually, however, she cheered up and whistled a happy song as she moved on to find new adventures.

23rd November

Nibbling Helen

On the wall hung a cupboard that was too high for Helen to reach. Her parents had put it up there for a reason, for it was the medicine cupboard. But because there was no one around she got a chair so that she could open it. She opened all the bottles and started nibbling on the pills. Her little sister Alex said, "I don't think you should be eating those, they're medicine!" But Helen kept on nibbling and told her to be quiet. Later on she had terrible stomach-ache and was sick all day, for medicine is a good thing when you take it in the right doses, but don't ever take it yourself, children, because look what happened to Helen!

24th November

Pennies from Heaven

There was once a little orphan girl who was so poor that she didn't even have a room or a bed, and soon all she had was the clothes she wore and a piece of bread that a kind neighbour had given her. But she was a very good and holy child, and because she was deserted by the whole world, she put her faith in God and went out into the fields. There she met a poor old man who said to her, "Oh, please give me something to eat, I'm so hungry!" The good-hearted little girl gave him her only piece of bread, said "God bless you," and went on, she was so glad that she had been able to help the man. Then she met a child who said to her, "I'm so very cold, please give me something to

cover my head!'' The little girl felt so sorry for the child that she gave it her hat. Later on she met two other children who were cold, and she gave one her bodice and the other her skirt. By night time the girl had reached a wood, and there she met another child who asked her for her blouse, and because it was night and no one would see her, she gladly gave the child her blouse. So there she stood in the dark wood with nothing in the world except her underskirt. Then, all at once, golden stars fell from the sky, but the stars were big gold coins. Her underskirt turned into a beautiful dress of the finest linen, and in this dress the child gathered the coins and was rich for the rest of her life.

25th November

The Horse on the Church-tower

I rode to Russia in the middle of winter. This season is the best for travelling, but unfortunately I was too lightly clad to be comfortable. Towards evening I looked for somewhere to stay, but there were no

One day, when he's riding in a forbidden area, he crashes into a woman before he can put on his brakes. He knocks the lady down as well as himself and tears her new dress, and sends all her shopping rolling over the pavement. Now he has to pay for a new dress and all the lady's spoilt shopping. His piggy-bank is completely empty and that hurts more than his cut knee. That's the last time he'll ever ride on the pedestrian way.

27th November

The Poster man

On the big advertisement boards are hung many posters. From time to time the poster-man comes and takes them all down to stick new ones there, for he drives around all day with his glue-brush. Fast as lightning he tears one down and wipes his glue brush over the new one. The biggest posters are in two parts and have to be stuck together. Today the poster-man has brought his son with him. There's going to be a pantomime in the theatre and he's got to stick up four big posters advertising this. His son says that he can do it on his own. Now he can manage the small posters very well, but he makes a mess of the big one which is in two parts. He has stuck them together wrongly, and now Little Red Riding Hood has the legs of Puss in Boots. The children will be very surprised when they see that!

28th November

Snow-White (1)

There was once a Queen who gave birth to a daughter whose skin was as white as snow, whose lips were as red as blood and whose hair was as black as coal, and so they called her Snow-White. The

houses for miles around, and there was nothing but snow as far as the eye could see. So I tied my horse to a tree-trunk and lay down to sleep. The next morning I thought I was dreaming! I was lying near a Church and my horse was whinneying above me. The snow had melted overnight and I had sunk down with it. I had tied my horse to a Church tower, so I had to shoot my horse free before we could continue.

26th November

Harry Sizzlewind

Harry Sizzlewind is a wild, naughty child. He just zooms along on his scooter all day and doesn't have any respect for anyone. He even rides along on pedestrian areas where he's not supposed to.

214

Queen died, and within a year the King had married again. The new Queen was very beautiful, but proud and vain. She had a magic mirror, and whenever she looked into it she asked it, "Mirror, mirror on the wall, who is the fairest of them all?" and the mirror would answer, "You are the fairest of them all." But Snow-White grew up, and one day when the Queen asked the mirror her question, the mirror replied, "Snow-White is the fairest of them all." The Queen was shocked, and couldn't bear the thought that anyone should be more beautiful than she. From that moment on she hated Snow-White, and was determined to get rid of her. So one day she ordered a hunter to take Snow-White in to the wood and kill her, and to bring back her heart. But the hunter let her go.

Snow-White (2)

Snow-White wandered around in the wood for a long time, until she came to a little house. In the house she found a table set with seven plates, seven knives and forks and seven cups, and along the wall stood seven little beds. Because she was so hungry, she ate a little from each plate and drank a little from each cup, then lay down on one of the beds and went to sleep. Soon afterwards the seven dwarfs who owned the house came home. They were angry that someone had eaten their food, but when they saw the beautiful sleeping Princess, their hearts melted, and they watched her peaceful sleep. The next morning, when Snow-White woke up, she told them what had happened to her. They felt so sorry for her that they said, "If you cook for us and look after the house, you can stay with us!" And so she did, and how happy they were! Now the wicked Queen, all the time thinking that Snow-White was dead, went to her mirror and asked her question, but the mirror replied, "With the seven dwarfs by the seven mountains tall, Snow-White is the fairest of them all!" The Queen was so furious that she decided to kill Snow-White herself, so she disguised herself as an old woman and went to her. Snow-White didn't recognise the wicked Queen, so she let her into the house. She bought a belt from her, but when the Queen tied it on for her, she tied it so tight that Snow-White couldn't breathe and she fell down as if dead. When the dwarfs came back they undid the belt so that she could breathe again. But the Queen soon discovered from her mirror that the girl was still alive, so she disguised herself in a different way and took with her a basket of wares. She offered Snow-White a comb that was so beautiful that she couldn't resist it, but the comb was poisoned, and as the wicked stepmother dug it into her hair, Snow-White sank to the floor in a dead-faint. The dwarfs were horrified and tore the comb from her hair so that she recovered, and they forbade her to let anyone in again. When the Queen found out she decided to use more cunning, and she disguised herself again, this time as an old market woman who carried an apple, half of which was poisoned. Snow-White refused to buy any of her wares, but the Queen said, "Let me at least give you an apple as a present. See, it's alright!" and she took a bite from the unpoisoned side. But as soon as Snow-White took a bite from the other side, she fell dead to floor.

The Queen cackled, "Let's see the dwarfs help you this time!" and flew off. When the dwarfs came back, they tried everything to bring Snow-White back to life, but it was all in vain.

30th November

Snow-White (3)

The dwarfs now lived in deep sorrow, and they built Snow-White a glass coffin so that they could always see her. One dwarf always kept guard while the others were at work. Then one day a Prince rode through the wood, and when he saw the beautiful girl he was so overcome with her charm that he begged the dwarfs to let him have the coffin. The dwarfs didn't want to part with her, but because the Prince was so earnest and promised to guard her with his life, the dwarfs agreed. But while they were trying to load the coffin onto his horse, one of them slipped and Snow-White banged her head against the edge of the coffin. The knock caused the piece of poisoned apple to dislodge itself from her throat and Snow-White lived again! The beautiful girl opened her eyes and said, "Where am I?" The dwarfs told her everything, took her out of the coffin and cried for joy that she was alive again. From then on the Prince visited her every day, until one day he went down on his knees and begged her to marry him, for he couldn't live without her. Snow-White agreed gladly, but the wicked Queen died of shock when her mirror told her that Snow-White was again the most beautiful in the land.

1st December

The Dear Little Sunny Ray

Now it's really winter time,
With December's snow-white dress,
But I shall throw a crown of gold
Upon that place of rest,
Where in a stable lies a child,
With parents standing by,
And through the window I shall shine,
But the baby will not cry.

2nd December

The Snowflakes

There was once a little raindrop sitting up in a big dark cloud who wasn't allowed to go down. All his brothers and sisters had already done the journey to the earth, but he wasn't allowed to. So the little raindrop cried bitter tears, and he cried many little raindrops that made the cloud quite wet. "You're a very ungrateful child," said the cloud, "because I've always treated you well." But the raindrop couldn't stop, so the cloud told the wind that he wanted to send this naughty child to Earth. "Well, I can do that," said the wind. "But the Earth is very cold and the raindrop would freeze." But he still wanted to go, so the wind blew with both cheeks until the raindrop and all his little tears fell from the cloud. But the raindrop didn't get far, for it was so cold on the Earth that the air was too stiff.

But the wind took pity on the little raindrops, and he wrapped them up in little cotton-wool balls and whirled them down to Earth. It was dark down there, for the sun had gone down and the moon was hiding behind a cloud to keep himself warm. So the raindrops and the tears huddled together on the cold ground so that all the ground was white. The next morning the children looked out of the window and cried, "Mummy, it's snowed overnight!" and they all rushed out to build snowmen and go sledge-riding. When the raindrop saw that, he thought about the cloud and why he had to wait for so long, for he was to have a different life from his brothers and sisters.

3rd December

Bells Never Ring so Sweetly

The bells shall never ring so sweet,
As now at Christmas time,
It is as though the Angels sing,
With heavenly voice sublime.

Just as they sang that Holy Night,
When the shepherds saw a blinding light,
The humblest of all, they were the first,
To spread the good news on the Earth.

4th December

The Seven Ravens

A man once had seven sons. He longed for a daughter, and at last his wife gave birth to a little girl.
But the baby was very weak, and she needed some water. The father sent one of the boys to the spring to get some water. All the others went with him, and because they all wanted to be the first to get the water, they dropped the jug in.

Now they were afraid to go home. When the sons didn't come back, their father thought they must have been too busy playing, so he said angrily, "I wish they'd all turn into ravens!" Scarcely had he said these words when he saw seven ravens flying around the house. The man was very sad, and his only comfort was his daughter, who gradually got stronger and more beautiful. For a long time the girl didn't know anything about her brothers, but one day she asked why she didn't have any brothers and sisters, and her parents couldn't keep it from her any longer. So her parents told her the story, but said it was fate and not her fault. But the girl just had to free her brothers, so one night she ran away, taking nothing but her ring, some bread and a jug of water. She went right to the end of the world, to the sun, but it was too hot; to the moon, but there it was too cold, so she ran quickly to the stars.
They were good and friendly, and the morning star gave her a little key and said, "Your brothers are in the glass mountain, and with this key you can get in." So the girl took the key and walked until she came to the glass mountain. With the key she happily opened the door. A dwarf came towards her and asked her what she wanted. "I'm looking for my brothers the ravens," she said. "The ravens aren't at home," said the dwarf, "But you can wait until they come back." As the dwarf set the table for their supper, the girl took some food from each plate, and on the last plate she left her ring. Then the ravens flew back, and when they went to their plates they each said, "Who's been eating from my plate? It looks like the mark of a human." Then the seventh one found the ring and said, "If only our sister were here, she could save us." Then the girl stepped forward and as soon as they saw her they resumed their human form. They all hugged each other and went happily home.

5th December

Softly Falls the Snow

Softly falls the snow,
With a holy glow,
Christmas-like the old wood shines,
As we await the Heavenly Child.

And as I strolled through falling snow,
A voice called out to me,
"Come, helper Rupert, lift your feet,
And deck this Christmas tree."
For now's the time when young and old,
Stop running in life's race,
And I'll fly round the whole world's globe,
At my speedy Christmas pace."

6th December

Servant Rupert

Out of the wood I came today,
For I saw the golden lights,
And up above from Heaven's door,
I saw the Christmas Child.

7th December

Frog Hobbleleg (1)

It was on a fine winter's day, and the sun was as yellow as honey in the sky. While the children were having a snowball fight, suddenly the ice broke on the pond: Frog Hobbleleg had woken up from his winter sleep. Little Tony saw him first and called. "Look, everyone! Frog

her gran when someone called behin[d] them, "Look out, I'm coming!" And Fro[g] Hobbleleg had already flashed pa[st] them, he didn't want to miss the next ri[de] on the roundabout, and – *hop!* – there h[e] was on the horse.

Hobbleleg's back!" Gradually the weather got warmer.
One night when Tony was dreaming in bed, the moon sent its rays through his window as though it wanted to say, "Wake up, Tony, there's something outside worth seeing." But Tony didn't wake up, so he didn't see how Frog Hobbleleg was sledging, and how when he reached the end of the snow he went flying into the pond! Spring had come, and little Kate was going for a walk with

8th December

Frog Hobbleleg (2)

At last it was holiday time, and this yea[r] Trish and Simon wanted to have a ride i[n] a balloon. There Aunty had invited the[m]

to stay with her in the town, and the[y] wanted to take the frog with them. Bu[t] Hobbleleg was too afraid to ride in th[e] balloon, so he took the train. What a lot [of] traffic at the train station! Frog Hobblele[g] just couldn't find his way round at al[l.] "Where's the exit?" he asked th[e] astonished train driver. The frog loved [it] in the big town. There were so man[y] interesting things to see. But the holiday[s] were over all too soon, and Trish an[d] Simon had to say goodbye. Fro[g]

Hobbleleg went with them in the train saying, "Now it's back to my friends!" They were already waiting for him by the pump. "Give us some fresh water!" they

begged, so the frog pumped some up for them. When it was winter he said goodbye to his swallow friends who now had to fly to the south. "See you next year!" he called to them. Soon snowflakes were floating down from the sky. Frog Hobbleleg sat on his sledge and called to the children, "Be good children and you'll get lots of presents under your tree!"

9th December

The Kitten Angel

One Sunday before Christmas, Penny's parents took her into town to go shopping. Mum wanted to take Penny to the Christmas market, so they separated from dad who had other things to do. Penny was quite overwhelmed with all the decorated streets, and wide-eyed she stared at the garlands made out of fir-

trees, the gold and silver baubles, the wax angels, the shining stars. A tall Christmas tree had been erected in the marketplace, which shone with many electric candles.

Then came the wonderful things on the stalls, and Penny was quite delighted. Later they met up with dad again in a cake-shop, and Penny ate a honey cake and drank hot chocolate. She had really rosy cheeks. "Now, Penny, what did you like best?" asked dad. "The kitten angel," said Penny straight away. "Where did you see that?" he asked. "At the market," said Penny, "He sat up in the Christmas tree and had a lovely face." But dad said, "There isn't an Angel at the market, you must have imagined it." But Penny was quite certain. So they went back to the market and Penny cried, "Look, there it is up there!" And right at the top of the Christmas tree sat a kitten looking fearfully down. Then a woman from a stall said, "Oh, there it is! It's been running around here for a few days. I was going to feed it but then it disappeared." She called her son and he fetched a ladder to bring the shivering animal down. Penny took it in her arms and warmed it up. The woman brought it some milk which it greedily lapped up. Soon it lost its fear and began to purr happily. "Please, mummy and daddy, please may I keep it?" begged Penny.

"I wouldn't want anything else for Christmas!" Her parents would have let her, but her mother said, "Perhaps the kitten has got lost and belongs to another little girl who's sitting at home crying because he's lost, so first of all we'll have to take it to the police-station." But no one claimed him, so Penny was allowed to keep him. He got a soft basket and warm sweet milk every day, and thanks to Penny he was never cold or hungry again. His own way of thanking her was to love her with his whole heart. Under the tree on Christmas day, Penny also found a new doll!

10th December

Mrs. Hill (1)

A widow had two daughters. One was beautiful and hard-working, but the other was ugly and lazy. However, the mother loved the ugly one better because she was her real daughter, and the other one had to do all the housework. In the evenings she had to sit by the fountain and spin until her fingers bled. Now it happened that once the spool got so bloody that she dipped it in the water to wash it, but all at once it jumped out of her hand and fell into the water. She ran to her stepmother in tears and told her of her misfortune.

But she was angry and said, "If you've dropped the spool in the water then you'd better get it back!" The girl went back to the fountain, crying bitterly, and in her despair she jumped in. She became unconscious, and when she woke up she was lying on a lovely meadow. The girl got up and explored and she found an oven full of bread. The bread called, "Pull me out or I'll burn," so she took it out. Later on she came to a tree full of red apples, and the tree called to her, "Shake me, please! All my apples are ripe." So the girl shook the tree until they had all fallen off. Eventually she came to a little house out of which looked an old lady, and the lady said to her, "Stay with me, dear child, if you work hard I'll take care of you. Just make sure you shake my bed so that the feathers come out, for then it will snow on the Earth. I'm Mrs Hill." So the girl stayed with her.

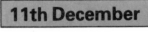

11th December

Mrs. Hill (2)

The diligent girl worked happily for Mrs Hill, and she shook her bed so that the feathers flew like snowflakes. But after a while she got homesick, and she said to Mrs. Hill, "Even though I've been very happy here, I can't stay any longer, I want to go home." Mrs. Hill understood, and she even accompanied her a little way

They had to go through a door, and as the girl stood beneath it, there fell a heavy rain of gold which covered her. "That's for you," said Mrs. Hill, "because you have worked so hard." And she pushed her through the door. On the other side she found herself not far from her mother's house. The cock by the fountain crowed, "*Cockadoodledoo!* Our golden young lady's back!" Then she went back home, and because she was covered in gold they greeted her amiably. When she told them of her good fortune, her stepmother wanted her own daughter to be so lucky, so she sent her off to the fountain, where she jumped in.

12th December

Mrs. Hill (3)

When the lazy girl had jumped into the fountain, she came to the same meadow and followed the same path. When she got to the oven and the bread called, "Take me out or I'll burn!" she said, "As if I'm going to get my hands dirty!" and went off. Soon she came to the apple tree, and when it called, "Shake me, my apples are all ripe!" she replied, "Not a hope! One of them could fall on my head!" and off she went again. When she got to Mrs. Hill's house she offered her services.

On the first day she worked hard and did everything Mrs. Hill told her, but from the second day onwards she got lazier and lazier until in the end she didn't want to get up at all. She didn't shake the beds hard enough so that the feathers flew, and that was serious. So then Mrs. Hill asked her to leave. The lazy girl was pleased and thought that now she would get her rain of gold. But when she stood under the door, a rain of pitch fell on her. "That's your wages!" said Mrs. Hill, and closed the door. When the cock on the fountain saw her he crowed, "Cockadoodledoo! Our dirty young lady is back." The pitch clung to her for the rest of her days.

13th December

Mrs. Hill and the Farmer

Once, many many years ago, Mrs. Hill went to Earth over Christmas to see if the people worked hard and were ready to help each other. She met a farmer who had been chopping wood in the forest and was walking tiredly home. Mrs. Hill said to him, "Bring your axe and mend my cart, otherwise I can't go on any further and it's such a cold night!" The farmer did what she asked and when he had finished Mrs. Hill said to him, "Pick up the sawdust that you have made from my cart. That is your reward.
Then she drove off. The sawdust seemed quite useless to the man, so he only picked up some of it. When he got home and emptied his pockets he found the sawdust had turned into gold. He turned straight back and went to fetch the rest, but it had gone.

14th December

Every year . . .

Every year the Christ-child comes
And mingles with the Earth,
He waves a blessing on every house,
And fills the world with mirth.

15th December

The Elves and The Shoemaker

There was once a cobbler who was so poor that he only had enough leather to make one more pair of shoes. In the evening he cut out the shape of the shoes to sew them the next day. But when he came down in the morning, the shoes were already made and standing on the table. The shoes were a masterpiece, with not one wrong stitch. They were soon sold, and the buyer was so pleased with them that he paid twice as much for them as normal. This meant that the cobbler could buy enough leather for two pairs of shoes. The next morning the same thing had happened, and so it went on until the cobbler could earn his living properly and he soon became a wealthy man.

Shortly before Christmas he said to his wife, "Why don't we stay up tonight to see who has been helping us all this time?" So they hid themselves in a corner of the room behind some coats. When it struck midnight, in came two tiny naked men who sat down on the table and started sewing and banging with such skill that the cobbler couldn't believe his eyes. When they had finished they sprang away. The cobbler's wife said, "Those little men have made us rich and we ought to thank them for it. I know! I'll make them a completely new set of clothes and you can make them some shoes." So they did, and the next night when the little men found their new clothes and shoes, they were absolutely delighted. "Aren't we fine fellows!" they said, "Far too good to be cobblers." And so that night when they went out of the door, they never came back, but the cobbler was now rich anyway.

16th December

The Angel with the Golden Nose (1)

Up on a big cloud, there are many little angels busy preparing for Christmas. All over the place there are golden nuts and little parcels tied up with red ribbons.

Whenever the Angels come out of the Christmas kitchen, they are always followed by the most beautiful smell. Everybody's mouth keeps watering, but the Angels are not allowed to nibble anything, because it's all meant for the children on Earth. Suddenly everything goes quiet because Saint Nicholas has come, and his face is shining with

ache. Nicholas kindly takes her by the hand and takes her to the chemist where she has to swallow some horrible medicine. Later on they practise their singing, but someone is playing out of tune, and of course it's the greedy little Angel. "You're too young to play yet," says Nicholas, and he takes away her flute. She sulkily sits on the edge of a cloud and dangles her legs over the edge watching the snowflakes dance to the music.

17th December

The Angle with the Golden Nose (2)

pleasure. "You've done everything so nicely," he says "But when you've finished we must practise our carols." Then his eyes fall on the smallest Angel, whose face is covered in gold, even her nose, and she's crying. Her dress is covered with crumbs and she's surrounded by nut shells. She hasn't covered them with gold but eaten them all, and now she's got terrible tummy

She bends over to get a better look and falls head over heels down to Earth. Thank goodness her wings give her a safe landing. She lands near a small village where a warm golden shine comes from every window. She flies up to one window and peers curiously in. A little boy has just received his Christmas presents. The candles on the tree shine so brightly that the little Angel presses her golden nose right up against the window. All at once the boy sees her and runs to the window. "Mummy!" he calls, "there was an Angel at the window, just look at that golden spot!" Christmas night has just come and the people stream into Church. The little boy is

going too, and suddenly he sees a trail of gold leading right up to the Church. "Look, mummy!" he cries excitedly. "The Angel must have been here." His mother just smiles. When in the Church he looks up at the wonderful ceiling, where there are many engravings of Angels – but that one's moving! The little boy holds his breath as an Angel looks down at him roguishly. Then she mingles in with the singing of *Silent Night* with her heavenly voice. In Heaven the little Angel is already missed.

When she comes back to Heaven for the Christmas service she has a lot to tell. How fascinated the other Angels are!

Neil the Cat

In a fishing village on a lonely island there lived a fisherman and his wife. They also had a beautiful silver-grey cat called Neil. He was greatly loved and his owners were so proud of the noble animal as he stalked through the grass making all the mice scatter. One evening the fisherman's wife said, "it's Christmas soon, and we ought to put something under the tree for Neil too." So they decided to give him a big sausage. On Christmas evening a great storm raged over the land, and the fisherman's wife looked anxiously out of the window for Neil. Then she heard a scratching, so she opened the window and in came Neil carrying something in his mouth, which he put down in front of her and looked at her pleadingly. She picked it up and it began to miaouw in her hands – it was a saturated tiny kitten! Neil had found it lying helplessly on the sand. The fisherman's wife rubbed it dry and wrapped it up in covers. Then she gave it warm milk, which it thirstily lapped up, and then she put it in Neil's basket.

The fishing people kept it and never let it out of their sight.

Oh Christmas tree!

Oh Christmas tree, oh Christmas tree!
How green and bright your branches.
You're not just green in winter time,
But also when the weather's fine.
Oh Christmas tree, oh Christmas tree,
How green and bright your branches!

20th December

The Three Feathers

There was once a King who sent his three sons out into the world, and the one who brought him back the finest linen thread would inherit his Kingdom. The King blew three feathers into the air which each fell in different directions, and each son was to follow a different one. One feather fell on a stone near the Palace and the youngest son, who was called Dummy, had to follow this one. He sat down on the stone and wept, for how was he going to find linen thread here? But suddenly the stone moved, and when Dummy looked down, he saw a staircase leading down to a cellar. There sat a girl spinning flax. Dummy told her his problem, and she gave him some of the finest linen thread. When he got back, he showed them his thread which was the finest of them all. But the King wasn't satisfied.

He gave them another task, and this time he demanded the finest carpet, but again Dummy's feather fell on the stone, so he moved it away and went down. There he found the girl very busy making a wonderful carpet out of golden threads. When it was finished the girl said, 'That was made for you, take it." So Dummy took it to his father and again was better than his brothers. But they persuaded their father to give them another task, so this time he promised the Kingdom to the one who brought back the most beautiful woman. Again Dummy's feather fell on the stone, and this time when he went down into the cellar, the girl told him to go in further and there he would find the most beautiful woman. So he did, and he came to a room shimmering with gold and precious jewels, but instead of a beautiful woman he found a frog. The frog called, "Kiss me!" At first he wouldn't but when he eventually did, he found himself holding the most beatiful woman in his arms. He took her to his father, who had to admit that she was a thousand times more beautiful than the women of the other two. But it still wasn't over, and now the women had to jump through a ring hung in the room. Since Dummy's lady was the only one who could do it, he inherited the Kingdom.

21st December

The Christmas Angels (1)

In the time before Christmas, there's always an awful lot to do, so much that St. Peter has almost forgotten it's Christmas Eve. "Good Heavens!" he cries. "Quickly, quickly, you Angels, pack your presents together and fly down to Earth!" Head over heels the Angels pour out of Heaven, loaded with parcels and trees, all looking forward to seeing the waiting children. There's a lot to do on Earth. An Angel flies to little David, who's been waiting for hours at the window. All the things he wanted he got: a train set, a car, a dog, all sorts of things. The little Angel had remembered everything he's written on his notepaper. "Oh, thank you, dear Angel!" says David happily. The smallest Angel is especially happy, for this is the first time she's been allowed to come with the other Angels; last year she was too young. Today she is to take little Mark his presents, and the little boy is lying in his cot. So the little Angel takes his puppet and lays it on his cot. Mark gurgles with pleasure as the funny puppet laughs down at him. When the Angel sees that Mark is tired, she flies away. The little Angel is very happy,

Christmas on Earth is even better than she'd imagined. The Angels fly from house to house and don't leave any child out.

22nd December

The Christmas Angels (2)

Even in the smallest cottages today there are happy children. On the edge of the town lives little Ruth, with her mother, and she writes a long list of things she wants. Her mother says, "Oh dear, I don't think the Angels will be able to afford all this, you'd better cross a few things out." So Ruth takes a pencil and crosses almost everything out, all except the Christmas tree, which she wants most of all. On Christmas Eve when Ruth goes into the living room the tree is a sea of lights, and underneath there are lots of other presents too. How happy Ruth is!

Now the sacks are empty and everything's been shared out. Quietly and happily the Angels float back to Heaven. "Let us in, Peter!" they call when they get to Heaven's gate. "Come in, come in, you must be so tired," they call when they get to Heaven's gate. "Come in, come in, you must be so tired," said Peter, "But tell me quickly, have you done your duty and made all the children happy?" "But, Peter," laughed the Angels, "if you're so suspicious, look through the hole you made in the wall!" "You rascals!" called Peter. But when they'd gone, he peeped through the hole onto the Earth. In the forester's house sit two little boys on the floor, absorbed in their game. They've made a wood out of pieces of trees, deers, hares and squirrels, and to them it's the real world. Peter steps back from his hole, satisfied. Night sinks down over the Earth, and a golden glow comes from every window.

24th December

Christmas in the Forest (1)

23rd December

Tomorrow, Children . . .

Tomorrow, children, how you'll jump
Out of your cosy beds,
Christmas presents, Christmas food,
And happy cheeks so red.
Then you'll sing, and then you'll play,
For tomorrow it is Christmas day!

Today it's Christmas eve, and all the roofs are covered in snow and shining in the falling sun. The branches of trees are bent down with the weight of the snow, and then Father Christmas appears. He leaves a bright trail of biscuits, apples and nuts in the snow, for there's a hole in his sack. But it's not long before they've all disappeared, for the animals soon gobble them all up. The only thing left is a pair of slippers, for they don't taste very nice!

But they take the slippers to the Pixie, for they may fit him. But when he tries them on they're much too big. "I know," said the Pixie, "we'll take them to the old lady who lives on the edge of the forest!" The animals thought this was a good idea, and so they all set off together.

25th December

Christmas in the Forest (2)

It's a long way to her house, but eventually they get there. The old lady hears such a strange scrabbling that she comes out to see what's going on. How astonished she is when she sees the lovely slippers on her doorstep! She moves her hand over the fine velvet, she's never had such a lovely pair of slippers. The animals have hidden themselves behind trees and bushes and they're delighted with the pixie's good idea. The lady goes inside to try them on, and the animals peer curiously in through the window. The shoes fit her as though they were made for her. The animals happily set off home, and on the way they meet Father Christmas. They tell him how they have given the old lady the slippers, and he's very pleased, for

the slippers were meant for her anyway. "Next year you can help me give out the presents," he said, "For then I wouldn't be as tired as I am today!"

"Great!" shout the delighted animals. "Goodbye 'til next year!" Then they all run to the Pixie's house. But what's that! They can hardly believe their eyes: there stands a beautifully decorated Christmas tree, a manger and a bird house. "Now I won't have to celebrate on my own," cried the Pixie. Then they all stand around the Christmas tree and sing. Christmas in the forest is the best thing of all, thinks the Pixie, as he looks happily at all his friends, whose eyes are sparkling with joy.

26th December

Oh you Joyful . . .

Oh you joyful, oh you Holy
Gracious Christmas day!
The world is not forlorn,
For Christ the Lord is born,
And took our sins away.

27th December

Sesame Mountain

There was once two brothers, one of
whom was rich while the other was poor.
The rich one gave his brother nothing, so
he had to earn a sparse living from selling
corn, and sometimes he didn't even have
bread for his wife and children. Once he
was driving through the wood when he
came to a big bare mountain which he
had never noticed before. Suddenly
along came twelve wild men. They went
up to the mountain and called, "Open
Sesame!" Then the mountain opened
up, the men went in, and then it closed
again. After a while they came back,
carrying heavy sacks, and they said,
"Close, sesame!" The mountain closed
and they went away. The poor man was
eaten up with curiosity, so he went up to
the mountain, called "Open Sesame!"
and when the mountain opened he went
in. The whole inside of the mountain was
made of gold and silver, and in every
corner lay precious stones. At first he
didn't know if he should take anything,
but in the end he filled his pocket with
gold. He went out and closed the
mountain, then he rode home in his cart.
Now they could have everything they
wanted, and when the gold ran out, he
borrowed a shovel from his brother and
took some more gold from the mountain.
But the rich brother had become jealous
of his brother's good fortune, and he
threatened him with the Law if he
wouldn't tell him where he got his gold
from, so the poor brother had to tell him.
The rich brother at once harnessed a
carriage and rode to the mountain. He
opened the mountain and loaded his
carriage with as much treasure as he
could.
But in his greed he forgot the name of the
mountain and couldn't open the door. In
the evening the twelve wild men came,
and they laughed wickedly when they
saw him there. "So thief, we've found
you at last!" they cried. The rich brother
cried, "But it was my brother who stole
all your gold!" But no matter how much
he begged for his life, the thieves didn't
believe him and they cut off his head!

28th December

The Story of the Year (1)

It was in the last days of January when a terrible snow storm began. Everyone tried to shelter under their blankets in the carriages which were now finding difficulty in moving. When at last the snow stopped and there was a narrow path free of snow running along the houses, everyone just stood there, each one unwilling to make the first footsteps in the deep snow, to cross to the other side. By evening the sky was clear again, but now the snow froze so that it cracked when you trod on it. How the sparrows froze. "*Cheep, cheep,*" they feebly said, "so this is the new year, and it's worse than the last one, we'd have done better to keep it!"

One very old sparrow with white hair said, "The humans have something called a calendar, and they reckon from that, that this is the beginning of the year. But Nature reckons that Spring is the beginning, and I'm sticking to that!" "But when does Spring come?" asked the others. "It comes when the stork comes," answered the old sparrow. "But it'll be rather uncertain here in the town, for here isn't a stork. Shall we go out into the country, for I'm sure spring will come sooner there." So they all flew into the country. But there it was even colder than in the town, and the sharp wind blew over the snow-clad fields. The farmer, wearing thick gloves, kept slapping his arms together to keep himself warm as he drove around on his sleigh. The thin horse ran with steam coming out of his mouth, and the hoof traces he made in the snow froze straightaway. Weeks went by, and then a feeble ray of sunshine appeared over the lake. Slowly the snow sank into the fields and here and there you could see a piece of green. The sparrows excitedly cheeped, "Is Spring here now?"

29th December

The Story of the Year (2)

Spring spread all over the fields and meadows, and through the dark brown woods in which the moss shone bright green on the tree trunks. From the south flew in the first two storks, and on the back of each one was a little baby. They

landed on the ground and kissed it, and wherever they touched, white flowers sprang up. The two children went hand in hand to the old snowman Winter and took his hand. At that moment they all disappeared, and a thick mist covered the whole countryside. A little while later a breath of wind blew all the mist away and the sun shone warmly. Winter had disappeared and the two beautiful children of Spring sat on the Year's throne. Wherever they walked, blossoms bloomed on the hedges, the grass grew higher and the fields greener. All round the little girl sprinkled flowers, for her dress overflowed with them. So the weeks went by and warmth streamed down to Earth. Hot heat-waves flowed through the corn, making it more and more yellow. Then heavy rain fell which wouldn't stop, but soon it turned into single drops and the sun shone and the birds sang again.

But that wasn't all: The fish began to jump, the midgets danced, and out there on the rocks in the salt-whipped sea sat Summer himself, the strong man made young again in the fresh water.

The Story of the Year (3)

Dear and sweet was the air that waved over the fields. The bees buzzed, the blackberry stems wound themselves round the sacrificial altar that was gleaming in the sunlight. The Queen bee flew there with her swarm and put down her wax and honey. No one could see the altar except Summer and his powerful wife, for them alone stood the altar with the offerings from nature. The apple-tree boughs bent under the weight of its yellow and red apples. Under the hazelnut bush decked with thick bunches of hazelnuts sat Summer and his serious wife. "What a Kingdom," she said, "It's filled with blessings, and yet, I don't know why, I long for peace and quiet. Now the people are harvesting their fields wanting to get as much as they can

Do you remember when we both went to the north as children. There the wind made the trees beautiful with gold and brown, and we could rest under their dark shade."

"Is that what you miss?" said Summer so he raised his arm and coloured the leaves with red and gold, and the woods shone with the most beautiful colours. But his wife got paler and paler and she said, "It's getting colder! I long for the place of my childhood." And the woods got yellower and yellower, leaf after leaf fell from the tree, thick fog came, the icy wind and the long long nights. There stood the Year's master with his long white beard.

The Story of the Year (4)

The Church bells announced the arrival of Winter. "They are the bells of birth," said the old man. "Soon the new Master of the Year will be born, and I can go to my rest among the many stars." And in the fresh green fir-tree wood, in the snow, stood the Christmas Angel waving the young trees. "Peace between the green branches," said the old man. "The time of rest is drawing near. These past weeks have made me ancient, and the new Master will come and take my sceptre and crown. "But you still have the power," said the Angel, "Only until the end of December, and then I will be free," said the old man.

And with white hair and long beard, he sat on a snowy hill looking towards the South, where last year the other Master had looked. The ice-skaters slid over the frozen lake, and the ice made cold bridges all through the land. The master dreamed of his youth, and his dream of his summer days made the sun shine and take the hoar-frost away. "When's Spring coming" asked the sprarrows, and their question echoed all over the hills where the snow still lay. The Bells announced the beginning of the New Year, and a thick cloud descended on the old man and took him away. The Story of the Year was over. The sun shone warmer and warmer, and through the air flew the first two storks carrying a child each on their backs. They bent down and kissed the Earth, and flowers began to grow.

STORY CALENDAR